D1209045

Green Light, Go

THE BANK STREET READERS

prepared by the

BANK STREET COLLEGE OF EDUCATION

SENIOR EDITOR *Irma Simonton Black*

MANAGING EDITOR *William H. Hooks*

ASSOCIATE EDITORS *Joan W. Blos, Betty Miles*
Jean Merrill, Betty Boegehold
Claudia Lewis

SKILLS CONSULTANTS *Frances M. Kerr*
Louise Matteoni

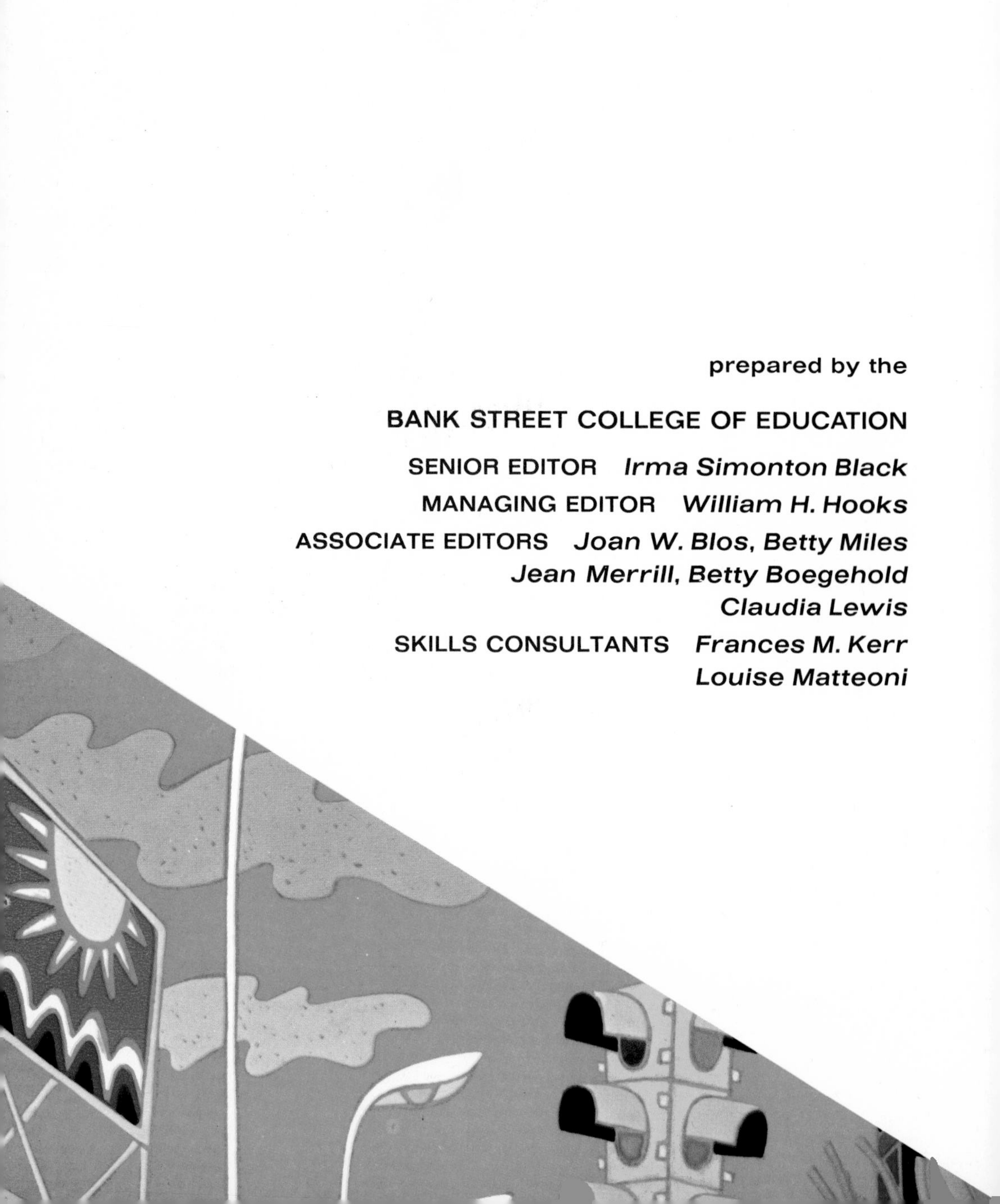

Green Light, Go

Revised Edition

BANK STREET COLLEGE OF EDUCATION

Illustrated by Jack Endewelt, Mamoru Funai, Ray Huebner, David Klein, George Mikolayczik, George Mocniak, June Otani, Robert Quackenbush, Donald Silverstein.

MACMILLAN PUBLISHING CO., INC.
NEW YORK
COLLIER MACMILLAN PUBLISHERS
LONDON

ACKNOWLEDGMENTS

Grateful acknowledgment is made to the following authors and publishers for permission to use copyrighted material:

Abelard-Schuman Ltd. for "The Seal Store" (originally "Seals for Sale"), reprinted from *Seals for Sale* by Carl Memling. Reprinted with the permission of Abelard-Schuman Ltd. All rights reserved, ©, 1963.

The Dial Press, Inc., for "Olaf Mails a Letter," adapted from *Olaf Reads* by Joan Lexau. Copyright ©, 1961 by Joan Lexau. Reprinted with the permission of the publishers, The Dial Press, Inc.

E. P. Dutton & Co., Inc., for "It's Raining" (originally "It Is Raining"), adapted from *Another Here And Now Story Book*, edited by Lucy Sprague Mitchell. Copyright 1937, by E. P. Dutton & Co., Inc. Renewal, ©, 1965 by Lucy Sprague Mitchell. Adapted by permission of E. P. Dutton & Co., Inc.

E. P. Dutton & Co., Inc., for "What Happened to Mike?" (originally "Where's George?"), adapted from *Believe and Make-Believe*, edited by Lucy Sprague Mitchell and Irma Simonton Black. Copyright, ©, 1956, by the Bank Street College of Education and E. P. Dutton & Co., Inc. Adapted by permission of E. P. Dutton & Co., Inc.

Harper & Row for "A Poem" (originally "Keziah"), from *Bronzeville Boys and Girls* by Gwendolyn Brooks Blakely. Copyright ©, 1956. Reprinted with the permission of the publishers, Harper & Row.

Holiday House, Inc., for "Night Cat" by Irma Simonton Black. Adapted by permission of Holiday House, Inc., © 1957.

MACMILLAN PUBLISHING CO., INC., 866 THIRD AVENUE, NEW YORK, NEW YORK 10022
COLLIER-MACMILLAN CANADA, LTD., TORONTO, ONTARIO

4-M

Printed in the United States of America

Contents

Part One

Part Two

Part Three

Part Four

Part One

City Boy, Country Boy

Two boys lived in different places.
They had different houses, different faces.
Their names were
Joe
and
Joe.

One Joe had red hair, one had brown.
One lived in the country, one in town.
One lived high up, one lived down.
They both were
Nine years old.

One Joe's house was new and high.
He could see the cars go by,
And trucks and buses.

One Joe's house was old and small.
There was no house next door at all,
Only grass and flowers.

Two boys,
Two different places,
Different houses,
Different faces.
Same names—
Joe
and
Joe.

My Name Is Not "Hey, You!"

Kate had moved many times. Now she had moved to another new street in another new city.

She looked out the window and saw many children she did not know. Then Kate put on her coat and went out into the street.

Some girls were jumping rope in front of Kate's house. As Kate watched them, one girl sang,

> "House to let—
> Inquire within.
> When I move out,
> Let Ellen move in."

The girl jumped out, and the girl named Ellen ran in. Kate moved nearer. No one looked at her. She moved still nearer to the turning rope. She wanted to jump very much.

Now Ellen sang,

"House to let—
Inquire within.
When I move out,
Let Carmen move in."

Carmen was ready to run in. But all at once Kate jumped in first.

"Hey, you! Who said you could jump in?" shouted Carmen.

Kate stopped jumping. She didn't know what to say.

"Go on — get out!" another girl said. "It's our rope."

The girl named Ellen pushed Kate out.

Kate wanted to stay and play with them. But what could she do? She made a face at the girls, and walked down the street.

A little way down the street, some boys were playing ball. Kate sat down on a step near them.

All at once the ball rolled right toward Kate. She put her foot on the ball to keep it from rolling.

"Hey, you!" the boys called. "Give us that ball. It's our ball!"

Kate really wanted to play. So she picked up the ball and ran away with it.

"Come and get it," she called.

The boys all ran after her. Kate turned and threw the ball back to them. Maybe they would play with her now. But the boys ran back down the street.

"Oh yah, yah, yah," Kate called as she walked on.

Down at the corner, some older girls were sitting together. Kate watched the girls for a while. Not one of them said anything to Kate.

Kate began to hop up and down. She hopped toward the girls and kept on hopping right up the steps.

"Hey, look!" called Kate. She hopped down the steps.

The older girls watched Kate. Then Kate almost fell and bumped into one of them.

"Hey, you!" a girl said. "Look out!"

"Show-off!" said another girl.

"Show-off yourself," Kate said.

The girls turned away from her and went on talking together.

Kate walked slowly back to her house.

How could she get to play with anyone around here?

Kate thought and thought. Then all at once she ran into her house as fast as she could.

In her house, she got some paper and made a sign. Then she took the sign and went back out to the street.

Kate walked up and down near the girls, carrying the sign.

"Hey, look," Ellen said.

All the girls turned to look at Kate's sign.

The sign said:

I AM NOT HEY-YOU.
MY NAME IS KATE.
WHAT'S YOUR NAME?

All the girls began to laugh.

"Hi, Kate," one girl said. "My name is Carmen."

"My name is Jean," said another.

"Mine is Ellen," said Ellen.

"Hi," said Kate. "I just moved here."

"Here, Kate," Ellen said. "You can take my end of the rope."

Kate smiled. She put her sign down on the sidewalk. Then she took the rope from Ellen, and she turned it as hard as she could.

Ellen jumped in. She sang,

> "House to let—
> Inquire within.
> When I move out
> Let Kate move in."

Quickly Kate handed the rope to Carmen. And Kate moved in!

Too Quiet

An old woman and an old man lived in a big city. One day they thought they would move.

"This city is too noisy," said the old woman.

"We will move to a quiet country place," said the old man.

So they moved to a quiet little house near a quiet little town in the country. No cars or trucks went by their little house. No children played there.

"The country is very quiet," said the old woman. "Maybe there is not quite enough noise for us."

"Yes," the old man said. "It is very, very quiet."

"Oh, dear," said the old woman. "We are not used to so much quiet."

They both felt a bit unhappy.

"Well, I can do something about that," the old man said.

He went to the little town. Soon he came back, carrying a cage.

"What do you have in that cage?" asked the old woman.

"A bird," said the old man. "Now we will have a little noise around here. Sing, bird, sing."

The bird sang. But he was quite a little bird, and he sang only soft little songs. The house was almost as quiet as ever.

"It is still too quiet here," said the old woman. "We are used to more noise than that."

"Well," the old man said. "I can do something else."

He went back to the little town. This time, he came back carrying a box.

"What do you have in that box?" the old woman asked.

"A kitten," said the old man. "Kittens make more noise than little birds do. Pat her and see."

The old woman patted the kitten. The kitten sat on the old woman's lap and purred. But she purred very quietly.

After that the kitten just walked around the house, had milk and fish, and mewed her soft little mew and purred her soft little purr. The house was almost as quiet as ever.

"Too quiet for us," the old woman said.

"Wait," the old man said. "I have another idea."

He walked to the little town once more.

"Now what is it?" the old woman asked when he came back with a box.

"A puppy," the old man said. "I know we will have real noise now. A puppy always makes a lot of noise. Call him and you'll see."

The old woman called the puppy. The puppy jumped and wagged his tail. He barked. But his barks were only soft little puppy barks.

The house was almost as quiet as ever.

"A bird, a kitten, a dog," said the old woman. "What else makes noise?"

They both thought and thought about it.

"I know," the old man said at last. He smiled. "I know just what we need."

He told the old woman his new idea.

She laughed. "Yes, yes," she said, giving him a hug. "That is what we really need."

"And that is what we will get," said the old man. "But first there are some things for us to do."

The old man made some penny toys and penny whistles. Next he painted the house door red. Then he put a big bell over the door.

The old woman made some cookies. Next she made some candy. Then she made a lot of ice cream.

And then the old man made two huge signs. Going to town, he put up one of the huge signs there. Coming back, he put the other sign on the red front door. It said:

ICE CREAM

PENNY TOYS   PENNY WHISTLES

PENNY CANDY   PENNY COOKIES

PETS TO PLAY WITH

The old man began to ring the bell over the red door. The sound of the bell went all the way to the town.

The old man and the old woman sat and smiled and waited.

All at once, they heard noise! It was the sound of feet running down the road.

There was another noise! It was the sound of children laughing.

The children came running to the Children's Store. They came to buy the penny cookies and the penny toys and the penny whistles. They came to eat ice cream and to play with all the pets that the old man and the old woman had.

Now the bird sang long high songs. The kitten purred and purred, and the puppy barked and jumped and wagged his tail. Laughing and shouting, the children called to one another. They blew the whistles that the old man had made.

The old man and the old woman smiled at each other. She gave him a hug, and he gave her a hug.

The noise was like music to them. At last their house in the country was not too quiet for them.

The Line Down the Middle of the Room

Victor and Billy were brothers.

"Look what you did!" said Victor to Billy one day. "You broke my plane!"

"I didn't mean to," Billy said.

Victor picked up his broken plane. "I told you not to get into my things," he said.

"I just wanted to see it," Billy said.

"This was my new plane!" Victor said.

He took Billy by the arm. "Say you're sorry."

"You can't make me say anything," said Billy.

Victor took something out of his pocket.

"See this roll of tape?" he said. "I'm going to put a line of tape right down the middle of the room!"

"What for?" Billy wanted to know.

"Wait and see," Victor said.

Then Victor made a line with the tape right down the middle of the room.

"Now," Victor said. "This is better."

"How come?" said Billy.

"Now you'll know which is your side and which is mine. I don't want you ever to step over that line. From now on, stay on your side!"

"Who cares?" Billy said.

When Victor got into bed that night, he forgot to turn off the light. Billy was still up.

"Hey, turn off the light, will you?" Victor asked.

"I can't," Billy said.

"What do you mean, you can't?" asked Victor.

"I can't!" Billy said. "I can't step over the line! The light is on your side."

"Oh, come on," said Victor.

"No!" said Billy. "I can't step over the tape. You said so yourself!"

Victor couldn't make Billy turn off the light. He had to get out of bed and turn it off himself.

In the morning, Victor felt cold. He saw that the window was open.

"Shut the window, Billy. I'm cold," he said.

"Well, I'm not," said Billy.

"Shut that window or I will!" said Victor.

"Oh no, you won't!" Billy said. "This is my side of the room. Remember?"

Just then the wind blew in. It blew the papers off Billy's desk. They flew all over the room.

"Hey, shut the window," Victor shouted. "And pick up your papers!"

Billy shut the window. Then he turned to Victor and smiled.

"But I can't pick the papers up," he said.

"Why not?" asked Victor.

"You know why."

Victor looked at the line of tape going down the middle of the floor.

"Oh, that crazy line!" Victor said.

He got out of bed and pulled the tape off the floor.

And that was the end of the line down the middle of the room!

What Happened to Mike?

The bright winter sun came in the window and woke the little boy. He ran to the window. He saw an old hat on the wet grass.

"Mike is gone!" the boy cried.

The boy ran to his father.

"What happened to Mike?" he asked.

"Mike who?" said his father.

The boy ran to his mother.

"Where is Mike?" the boy asked.

"Mike who?" his mother asked.

Then the boy asked his sister, "Do you know where Mike is?"

But his sister didn't know.

At last the little boy went to his big brother.

"Mike is gone!" he said.

"Poor Mike," his big brother said. "He just melted away in the sun. But when it snows again, we can make another snowman."

Saturday with Dave

I have no father. But I have a big brother. His name is Dave.

Dave works every day but Saturday and Sunday. Most Saturdays and most Sundays, Dave goes out with his friends. But sometimes he goes out with me!

Those days are the days I like best.

Yesterday was a day like that. It was Saturday. My brother was home. I went to wake him up. I always do that on Saturdays.

"Hey, Charles," he said. "How would you like to go out today?"

"With you?" I asked.

"Yes," Dave said.

"Just me and you?"

"Just the two of us," Dave said.

I knew it was going to be a wonderful day.

"Where are we going?" I asked Dave.

"Where do you want to go?" Dave asked.

"You mean we can go any place?" I asked Dave.

"Any place you want," Dave said.

So I said, "Let's go to the zoo."

"O.K.," said Dave. "We'll go to the zoo. But first we'll have a very big breakfast. There's nothing like a big breakfast for starting off a big day."

My mother made us a big breakfast. I ate one egg, and Dave ate three.

Then I got cleaned up, and my mother gave me some money so I could buy things at the zoo.

Then Dave and I walked three blocks to the bus. My friends saw me walking with Dave. They asked me where I was going. I said I was going to the zoo with Dave.

"I bet they wish they could come, too," I told Dave.

"Want to ask them?" he said.

But I said "No." It was better with just me and Dave.

Dave let me sit next to the window on the bus. It was a long way to the zoo, and the bus had to stop a lot. But I didn't care. I talked to Dave.

We got off the bus near the park. We walked through the park toward the zoo. It was cold, so we walked fast. Nobody walks as fast as Dave.

Dave saw a man with hot popcorn, and Dave got some. He got two bags! One for him and one for me. We ate the popcorn while we walked. Popcorn isn't any good if it isn't hot. That's what Dave says. This popcorn was very hot.

Then we came to the zoo.

Most of the animals were inside, because it was so cold. So we went inside, too. There were lions and foxes and monkeys in there.

The foxes were sleeping, but the monkeys were climbing all around in their cages. And one lion kept walking up and down. He walked slowly to one end of his cage, and he walked slowly back again.

Then Dave said, "Let's go outside." He said it smelled inside. It did. But I like that funny zoo smell. Zoos always smell that way.

Anyway, we went outside. It was still very cold, but the sun was bright, and the sea lions were swimming in the sea lion pool. They like the cold.

The sea lions were jumping in and out of the water. One jumped up so near that water splashed on me. Was that water cold!

The sea lion that splashed me made a funny sound, something like a dog's bark.

Dave barked right back at the sea lion, and all the people near the pool laughed.

Then I asked Dave if we could go to the part of the zoo where they let you pat the little animals. It's called the Children's Zoo. So we went over there, and I patted a little lamb. Then I got some animal food, and I gave some to the little lamb and to some deer. The deer came right over to me when I called them.

After that, Dave said it was time to go. On the bus going home, we went near a car that had eight dogs in it! There were so many dogs that I couldn't see the driver.

Dave said, "Maybe a dog is driving." Our bus driver laughed at that, and so did I.

When we got home, my mother was in the kitchen. She had a very good dinner ready for us. She had all the things that I like best. We had meat, potatoes, tomatoes, and ice cream. We had seconds on the ice cream. Dave and I were both hungry after our long day at the zoo.

After dinner, Dave went out with some of his friends, and I told my mother all about the day.

My mother liked hearing about it all. I liked telling about it. Dave says maybe we can do it again another Saturday.

Bob's Luck

Bob lived near a ball park.

When there was a baseball game, Bob and his friends wished they could go. But they didn't have the money.

One day, there was a big game. Bob and his friends sat on the steps of his house. One of the boys had a radio. They could hear cheering from the ball park.

Bob's mother came out with a shopping cart and a bag of laundry.

"Bob," she called, "Bob, would you please take this wash to the laundry?"

Bob said, "Do I have to go now? We want to hear the game."

"The game will still be going on when you get back," Bob's mother said. She put the laundry bag into the shopping cart.

"Oh, all right," Bob said. He pulled the cart down the street. In all the stores, radios were turned on to the game.

"BALL ONE!" said the man on the radio as Bob went by the candy store.

"BALL TWO!" the man on the radio called as Bob passed the bakery.

Some big boys were sitting in a car with the radio on. "BALL THREE!" said the radio as Bob passed the car.

Bob went faster. He wanted to get back home to hear the rest of the game.

When Bob was just outside the laundry, there was a big roar. It was the people in the ball park. Everyone in the park was cheering and shouting.

The roar came over the radio, too. The radio in the laundry was on.

The man on the radio was talking very fast. "It looks like a home run! The ball is going up, up, up — it's going out! Yes, it's out of the ball park!"

All along the street, people ran out of the stores to look over at the ball park.

"Look out!" a man on the street shouted.

And then—

Pow! Right into Bob's shopping cart—

Bob looked down. Everyone was running toward him.

"Hey, look!" Bob shouted. "I've got the ball! It fell right in my cart!"

"Hey, look!" a man called. "The kid got the ball. It fell right in his cart!"

Bob ran into the laundry.

"Hey, look!" he said to the laundry man. "It fell in my cart!"

He showed the ball to the laundry man. He pulled the cart over.

"I have to show this ball to the kids at home," he said. "Will you put the wash in for me? I'll come back for it later."

"Sure," said the laundry man. "So long, Lucky."

Bob ran all the way home. His friends were still there on the steps.

"Hey," called one. "Did you hear? The ball went right out of the ball park!"

"I know!" shouted Bob. He showed them the ball. "I got it! It fell in the cart."

"Right in?" asked one of the boys.

"Boy, you're lucky!" said another.

"It's my lucky day," Bob said.

Bob's mother heard all the noise and came out. Bob showed her the ball.

"See!" Bob said. "Look at it. A home run ball! Was I ever lucky to be there when it came down!"

"That's wonderful," said Bob's mother. "It's lucky I asked you to go to the laundry," she said.

Bob laughed. "It sure is," he said. "And it's lucky that I went!"

The Ox in the Box

An old man once said to an ox
Who was living with him in a box,
"Dear Ox, it would be
Much better for me
If you were only as big as a fox."

"War on Small Deer!"

A Very Old Story

One day Small Deer wanted to go to the other side of the river to eat the sweet fruit there. As soon as he came to the river, the crocodiles put their huge heads up out of the water.

"War on Small Deer! War on Small Deer!" they roared.

One crocodile rushed out of the water to bite Small Deer.

Small Deer pushed a small stick in the crocodile's mouth.

Then Small Deer cried, "You bit my leg. Let go! Let go!"

The crocodile was fooled. He thought the stick was really Small Deer's leg. So he bit down hard on the stick.

All the other crocodiles laughed. Now, when crocodiles laugh, they shut their eyes. When they had all shut their eyes, Small Deer ran away.

But he still wanted the sweet fruit on the other side of the river.

After a while, Small Deer came back to the river. He could not see any crocodiles there. But something was floating in the middle of the river. It looked like a huge, dark log. But could it be a crocodile?

"Are you a crocodile?" Small Deer asked the log.

No answer.

"Or are you just a big brown log?" Small Deer asked.

Still no answer.

"If you are a crocodile, you will float along with the water," said Small Deer. "But if you are a log, you will float the other way."

Small Deer watched.

Would it float along with the water? Or would it go the other way? Now, Small Deer knew that logs must always float with the water.

The dark thing began to move the other way! So Small Deer was sure this really was a crocodile, and not a log at all.

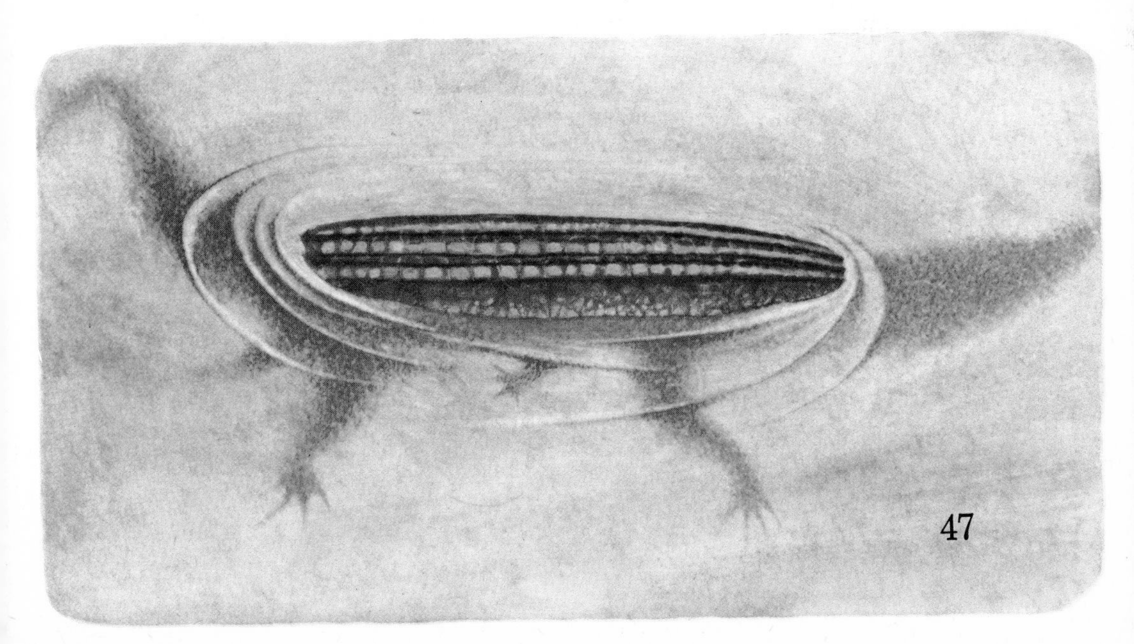

"Crocodile! Crocodile!" shouted Small Deer. "You gave yourself away. I fooled you!"

At once, all the crocodiles put their long heads out of the water and roared, "War on Small Deer! War on Small Deer!"

Small Deer still wanted the sweet fruit on the other side of the river. He had to think how he could get it.

The crocodiles did not go away. They just went down under the water. Here and there, Small Deer could see a crocodile nose sticking out.

Small Deer wanted that fruit very much. So he shouted again.

"Oh, you crocodiles, hear me! The King has sent me to count all the animals. The squirrels, the birds, the dogs, the lions and the foxes. I must count them all."

Then Small Deer went on, "The King will give a bag of gold to the animals who are bigger in number than any other kind. So come up and be counted, crocodiles. Who knows? You may be the lucky ones who win the gold from the King."

Crocodile noses began sticking up. One nose. Then another nose. Then another.

"Now do not move," cried Small Deer. "I must count you one by one. Let us see if you are bigger in number than all the other kinds of animals. Then you may win the gold!"

The crocodiles stayed very still.

Small Deer jumped on the nose of the first crocodile. "One!" he shouted.

"Two!" shouted Small Deer as he jumped on the nose of the second crocodile.

"Three, four, five!" called Small Deer as he jumped from crocodile nose to crocodile nose.

"Six, seven," Small Deer shouted from the middle of the river.

"Eight, nine, ten!" he shouted.

One more jump, and Small Deer was on the other side of the river.

"Good-by!" said Small Deer.

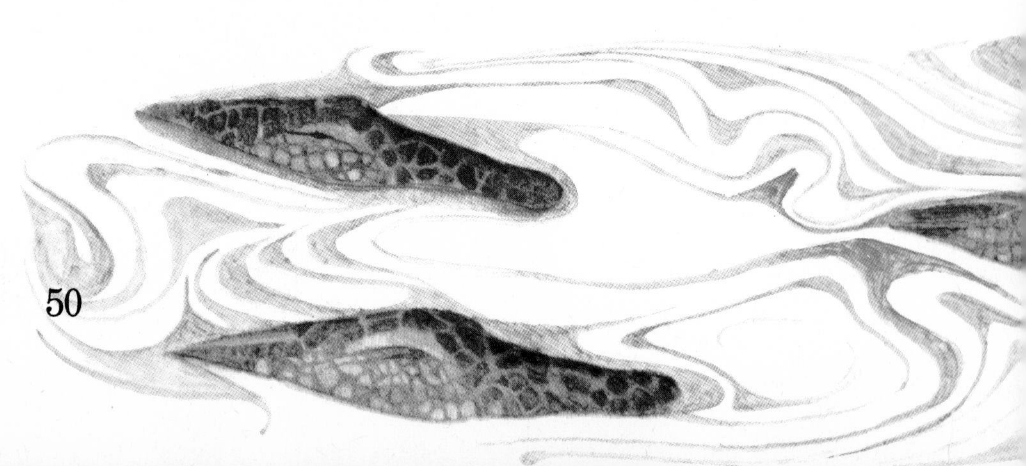

Now the crocodiles knew that Small Deer had played still another trick on them.

"War on Small Deer! War on Small Deer!" they roared.

But it did them no good. Small Deer was on the other side of the river, eating the sweet fruit.

Chicken Pox and Mumps

Charlie had the chicken pox.

Mary had the mumps.

Charlie had bumps.

Mary had lumps.

Mary couldn't go to school. Because mumps is catching. Charlie couldn't go to school, because chicken pox is catching.

So there they were, at home.

Charlie was home in Apartment 1-C.

Mary was home in Apartment 1-D next door.

Charlie wrote a note to Mary. His mother gave it to Mary's mother. The note said:

How are your mumps today?

Mary read the note. She wrote back:

The mumps make me look funny.
How are your chicken pox?

Her mother gave the note to Charlie's mother. Charlie read the note. The next day he wrote back:

Chicken pox itch. I can get out of bed, but I can't go to school.

He put his note under Mary's door.
Mary wrote back:

I can get up too. Can't you scratch the chicken pox?

Charlie wrote

My mother said not to.
Do mumps itch?

No, but they sure do look funny.

Let me see. Come to
the door.

Mary opened the door of 1-D.

Charlie opened the door of 1-C.

Charlie looked at Mary.

"You're right. You sure do look funny," he said.

Mary looked at Charlie. "Your chicken pox looks funny, too."

"How long do you have to stay home?" Charlie asked.

"Five more days," Mary said. "How long do you have to stay home?"

"Five more days, too. Too bad I don't have the mumps, like you. Then we could play together," said Charlie.

"Too bad I don't have the chicken pox like you," said Mary.

"Well," said Charlie. "Good-by, I don't want to catch your mumps."

"Good-by," said Mary. "I don't want to catch your chicken pox. So long. Don't scratch."

"So long. I won't," Charlie said. He went back inside 1-C. Mary went back inside 1-D.

Five days passed. Mary went back to school. And Charlie went back to school. They both felt fine.

But the next week, Mary had the chicken pox! And Charlie had the mumps! Mary had bumps. Charlie had lumps.

So there they were, at home again. But this time Charlie and Mary were lucky. They could play together.

Because once you have had chicken pox and mumps, you can't catch chicken pox and mumps again.

My Best Friend and I

My best friend and I,
We both like to talk.
My best friend and I
Like to walk and to talk.

We talk as we walk,
About this, about that.
A dog walks by.
And so does a cat.

Parades go by.
Fire trucks, too.
But we keep talking
As best friends do.

We walk and we talk
About her, him, and you.
The cat has kittens.
The kittens say, “Mew.”

Thunder comes.
Lightning flashes.
Rain comes down.
We talk between splashes.

Summer goes by.
So does Fall.
My best friend and I
Are growing tall.

Winter goes by.
So does Spring.
We go on talking
Like anything.

Look out on the street,
And what will you see?
Two girls talking—
My best friend and me!

My
name
is
Kate

DENVER

Part Two

The Scare House

One day Donna wanted something different. She was with her father in a different kind of park.

"I want to go to the Scare House," Donna said.

"Scare House?" said her father. "What's the Scare House?"

"It's full of things that scare you," Donna said. "Mary Ann told me about it." Mary Ann was Donna's best friend.

"Mary Ann says it's very dark inside the Scare House," Donna said. "And very, very scary."

"What about going on the Big Wheel?" asked Donna's father.

"No," said Donna. "I only want to go to the Scare House."

Donna's father paid some money. Then he and Donna got in line for the Scare House.

"When did Mary Ann go to the Scare House?" Donna's father asked.

"Oh, she never went," Donna said. "She almost went, but she was too scared. Mary Ann just *knows* about the Scare House."

Donna's father took a good long look at Donna. "Are you sure you want to go to the Scare House?" he asked.

"Yes," said Donna.

The Scare House door slowly opened with a creaky sound. It was very dark and scary inside. They bumped into something soft.

"Here," Donna's father said. "Take my hand."

Donna held her father's hand tightly.

"Don't be scared," her father said. "That witch isn't real."

Donna moved nearer to her father.

"That skeleton isn't real," her father said.

Donna moved even nearer to her father.

"Oh, look at the funny, big paper crocodile," Donna's father said. "Those lightning flashes and the thunder aren't real, either."

Donna went by the crocodile as fast as she could. She held on tightly to her father's hand. At last, they came to the creaky door again, and they went out into the bright sunlight.

"Are we outside?" said Donna. "Can I open my eyes now?"

"Donna!" her father said. "Were your eyes shut the whole time we were in the Scare House?"

"Yes," Donna said. "But don't tell Mary Ann."

Bigger and Bigger, Smaller and Smaller

A Very Little Play

A boy and a girl are talking.

MARY: I'm bigger than you.

JOE: Well, my sister is bigger than you.

MARY: I don't care. My mother is bigger than your sister.

JOE: My father is bigger than your mother.

MARY: Well — a giraffe is bigger than your father.

JOE: An elephant is bigger than a giraffe!

MARY: What about a dinosaur? Dinosaurs are bigger than elephants. They're the biggest things in the whole world.

JOE: Ha! There aren't any dinosaurs any more.

MARY: Anyway, you'd be very small next to a dinosaur.

JOE: I wouldn't *get* next to a dinosaur, ha, ha! Anyway, I'm not so small. My brother is smaller.

MARY: My little sister is smaller than your brother.

JOE: Well, a kitten is smaller than your sister.

MARY: O.K., but a mouse is much smaller than a kitten.

JOE: A fly! A fly is smaller than a mouse.

MARY: An ant! That's smaller than a fly.

JOE: A germ! A germ is much much smaller than an ant. A germ is so small you can't really see it.

MARY: But it could see me! And I'm bigger than you. So there!

This play can start all over again!

Not for Sale

The Four Puppies

There were four puppies in the window of the pet store.

In one box, three brown and white puppies played together.

But in a box by himself sat a little black puppy. Over his box was a sign: NOT FOR SALE.

Every time children passed by the pet store, the black puppy jumped at the window and barked and wagged his tail.

“Look!” called a boy on his way to school. “Look at that black puppy! That’s the puppy I want.”

“But he’s not for sale,” said the boy’s sister.

“How do you know?” asked the boy.

“Can’t you read?” said his sister. She pointed to a sign. “It says NOT FOR SALE.”

“Oh,” said the boy. “Well, why not?”

“I don’t know,” his sister said.

The boy pushed his nose against the window, and the puppy licked the glass on the other side.

“Look,” said the boy. “He wants to lick my nose. He wants to be for sale.”

“Well, he’s not,” his sister said. “Let’s look at the other puppies. They’re for sale. We could get one of those.”

The boy looked at the brown and white puppies. He put his nose against the glass near their box, and they ran over and jumped at the glass.

"They're nice, too," said the boy. "But I guess I like the black one best. He's the one I'd take."

"Come on," said his sister. "We have to hurry to school."

The boy waved good-by to the black puppy. The puppy wagged his tail and cried softly as the children went off down the street.

In a little while, a lady came to the pet store. She went inside.

"I want to buy a puppy for my little girl," she said to the old man who ran the store.

The old man showed her the brown and white puppies. "They're twelve dollars each," he said.

The puppies ran over and licked her hand.

"Oh, aren't they sweet!" said the lady.

The black puppy at the other end of the window began to bark.

"Oh, he's sweet, too," said the lady. She went over to the black puppy.

"I like this one best of all. May I have him?"

"I'm sorry, but that one isn't for sale," said the old man.

"Why not?" asked the lady.

"He's just not for sale," said the old man.

"That's too bad," said the lady. "Well, I guess I'll have to take one of the others." She picked out a brown and white puppy and held him in her arms.

"My little girl will love this one," she said. "But I wish the black one were for sale."

The old man gave the lady a box to put the puppy in. "You sweet thing," she said to the brown and white puppy.

She went over to pat the black puppy once more. As she turned to go, the puppy cried softly.

"I'm sorry I can't take you, too," the lady said to the puppy. "I would, if you were for sale."

The lady left and a man came into the shop.

"How much is that puppy?" he asked, pointing toward the black one.

"I'm sorry, but the black one isn't for sale," said the old man.

"What do you mean, not for sale?" the man asked.

"See, there's a sign over his box," said the old man. "I don't want to sell him."

"Why have you got him in the window, then?" asked the man. "If he's in the window, he should be for sale. This is a store, isn't it?"

"Yes," said the man. "I have lots of pets. Birds and kittens and fish and puppies. If you want to buy a puppy, I have two brown and white ones. You can have one for twelve dollars."

"But I want the black one," said the man. "How much is the black one?"

"I'm not selling him," the old man said again. "I'm sorry."

The man who wanted the black puppy was angry.

"I'm not buying *any* puppy," he shouted. "And I'm not coming in here again!"

The black puppy began to bark. He barked and barked at the man.

The man turned and went out the door. He made a big noise when he shut it. The black puppy kept on barking.

The old man went over and patted the puppy.

"There, there," he said. "You didn't want to go with him anyway."

In a little while a truck pulled up by the pet shop. The truck man opened up the back and took out some bags of dog food.

"Here you are," he said, carrying them into the store.

The black puppy barked.

"Hey," said the truck man. "I see you have some new puppies."

"Yes," said the old man. "That black one over there is not for sale. But the brown and white ones are."

The truck man picked up the black puppy. The puppy licked his ears.

The truck man laughed. "Hey!" he said. "Stop that." The black puppy wagged his tail. "Say, you like to play, don't you?" the truck man said.

He put the black puppy back. "It's too bad he's not for sale," he said.

Then the truck man looked at the two brown and white puppies rolling around in their box, playing together.

"Are those puppies for sale?" he asked. "They sure look happy."

"Yes," said the old man. "You can have one of those puppies for twelve dollars."

The truck man watched the puppies play. "It would be too bad to take just one of them," he said slowly. "They look so happy together."

"You can have both of them for twenty dollars," said the old man.

"I have two boys," said the truck man. "Two puppies would be just right for two boys! I'll take them both."

Now the black puppy was all alone in the store window. He cried softly. He barked and barked when he saw children on the street.

"There, there," said the old man to the puppy, as he began to shut up his store for the night.

The old man put the black puppy into a basket. He turned out the lights in the store, and took the puppy out to his car.

The old man drove for a long time.

The old man stopped his car by a big apartment house. He carried the puppy into the building, and he rang the bell on a door on the second floor. A girl came to the door.

The black puppy woke up and jumped right into her arms.

"Oh, Grandpa, what a sweet puppy! Is he from your store?"

"Yes," said the old man.

"Oh, Grandpa, are you going to sell him?"

"No," said the little girl's grandpa. "He's not for sale. He's for *you*."

"For me!" said the little girl.

"Just for you," said the old man.

The black puppy wagged his tail and licked the little girl's face. "Oh, I love him!" she said. "Thank you, Grandpa!"

The old man smiled as he looked at the girl and the puppy. The black puppy would never be for sale. Never!

Squeaky Sneakers

BOYS

Steve had sneakers.
Soft new sneakers.
The best kind of shoes in which to sneak.
But Steve's new sneakers
Were very squeaky sneakers.
And sneakers can't be sneaky when they
squeak.

Girls

Steve is late for school.
The bell has stopped ringing.
Steve runs fast in his nice new sneakers
To sneak in the door before the teacher sees him.
But he gets to his desk — and the sneakers *squeak*.
"STEVE!" calls his teacher. "Steve, you're late!"

Boys

Steve sees a cake
Just baked by his mother.
He runs into the kitchen in his soft new sneakers
To sneak up to the table and have a bite of cake.
He gets to the table — and the sneakers *squeak.*
"STEVE!" calls his mother. "Away from that cake!"

GIRLS

Steve runs to hide;
He's playing Hide-and-Seek.
He runs very fast in his soft new sneakers
To sneak in the closet and hide behind a coat.
But he gets to the closet — and the sneakers *squeak*.
"One-two-three on Steve!" And Steve is IT!

Girls and Boys

Steve had sneakers,
Soft new sneakers,
But they were not the best for Hide-and-
Seek.
For Steve's new sneakers
Were creaky, squeaky sneakers,
And sneakers can't be sneaky when
they squeak!

Wanted: One Bear, Two Sea Lions, Three Monkeys

The Middletown Zoo has many animals, but the zoo people are always looking for more. This year, the zoo needs one bear, two sea lions, and three monkeys.

Wanted: three monkeys.

Where can a zoo get three monkeys?

The zoo keeper asks some animal hunters to go to a faraway jungle where monkeys live. These men know everything about catching and taking care of animals. The hunters put a monkey trap in a tree. In the trap they put a banana. They put string around the banana and the trap. When a monkey picks up the banana, the string will pull the trap shut.

Soon a monkey comes along. He sees the banana. He runs toward the trap. He goes right in and takes the banana.

Bang! The trap shuts.

The men have been hiding nearby. When they hear the noise, they come and take the monkey out of the trap. They put him into a box. Then they put another banana in the trap to catch another monkey. Again they wait. After a while, another monkey comes into the trap, and after that, another.

The men take the monkeys they have caught to Middletown by plane.

A man from the zoo is waiting at the airport. He takes the monkeys to the zoo and gives them bananas. "Welcome to your new home," he says.

Soon people who work at the zoo will give names to the monkeys, and they will begin to feel at home there. Then the children of the town will come to see them.

Wanted: two sea lions.

Where can a zoo get two sea lions?

Sea lions live in the water most of the time. But they come up on to land to have their babies.

The keeper of the Middletown Zoo calls up a man who lives near an island where the sea lions come. Can he get two sea lions for the zoo?

The man answers, "Yes, I can get some sea lions for you. I'll send them as soon as I can."

Then the man goes out in a small boat with a friend.

They take a net with them.

When they get near the island, they put the net in the water. Soon three sea lions swim into the net. They try to get out, but they can't.

The men open the net and take the three sea lions out. But the Middletown Zoo needs only two sea lions. So the men let one of the sea lions go, and he splashes back into the water.

The men take the other sea lions home with them. They build a box for the sea lions, and put the box on a train.

In Middletown, a man from the zoo is waiting. He takes the sea lions to the big pool in the zoo, which is their new home. The sea lions are very happy to be in the water again. They swim around, barking to each other. The Middletown children will love to watch them.

Wanted: one bear.

How will the zoo get a bear?

The zoo keeper knows a very good way. He picks up the telephone and calls up the zoo in Park City.

"I hear you have a lot of bears, but no foxes," he says to the Park City Zoo. "We have lots of foxes, but no bears. If you'll send me a bear, I'll send you some foxes."

"Good!" says the man at the other zoo.

So the Middletown Zoo sends four foxes to the Park City Zoo. And Park City sends a bear to Middletown.

One new bear,
Two new sea lions,
Three new monkeys.

Now, the Middletown Zoo has all the animals it needs.

"Until next year," says the man who runs the zoo. "Next year we'll need an elephant!"

I Can Read

I used to get hit by the door
That opens itself at the store.
I used to begin
To use OUT to get IN
But I do not do that any more.
I can read!

The Girl Who Could Read in the Dark

"I can read," Maria said.

Jean laughed. Maria was only three. Jean was helping her get ready for bed.

"Listen," Maria said.

She took a little book called *The Three Bears*. Jean had read it to her many times.

Maria opened the book and looked at the pictures.

"This is the story about the bears," she said. "There is Mama Bear and Papa Bear and a little bear, and a little girl is going to come and break all their things. The little girl is Goldilocks."

"But you have the book upside down," said Jean. "You can't read it upside down."

"Yes, I can," said Maria as she looked at the book. "Goldilocks is breaking the little bear's chair. It's all broken."

"You're not reading," Jean said. She pointed to the word *Goldilocks*. "What is that word?" she asked.

"The word says that Little Bear is looking for his chair," said Maria.

Jean laughed and gave Maria a book she was reading in school. She turned to the story of *Jack and the Beanstalk*. "Here," she said. "Read this story."

Maria looked at the picture of Jack going up the beanstalk. "I don't know that story," she said. "I'll read some more about the bears."

"Come on," Jean said. "Get into bed."

"May I read in bed for a little while?" asked Maria.

"No," Jean said. "I have to turn out the light now. You can't read in the dark."

Jean turned out the light.

Maria said, "The little bear says, 'Who broke my chair?' See? I can so read in the dark."

Jean laughed again.

Mother heard Maria talking.

"Why isn't Maria in bed?" Mother called.

"She is," Jean said. "She's reading in the dark."

"In the dark? How can anyone read in the dark?" Mother asked.

"She just can," Jean said. "But we can't. You have to be little to know how!"

Puss in Boots

A Very Old Story

Puss Gets a New Master

Once upon a time, there were three brothers. When they grew up, their father gave something to each brother.

He gave the oldest brother gold. To the middle brother he gave a donkey. But the last brother got only a cat!

"What good is a cat?" he said. "I wish I had the gold, or the donkey. Then I could really be happy."

The cat, who was called Puss, heard what the last brother said.

"Don't feel bad, Master," said Puss. "Things are better than you think. You must do just two things. First get me a bag. Then buy some little boots for me. I will show you that I can bring you good luck."

The last brother did not see what the cat could do. But he got the things for Puss.

As soon as Puss got the little boots, he put them on. Then he put some food in his bag. And then he put the bag over his arm and went hunting.

When Puss came to a field, he lay down in the grass and opened his bag of food. Then he pretended to sleep. A rabbit came by. The rabbit smelled the food Puss had put into the bag, and he jumped right into the bag to get it.

Puss quickly pulled the strings on the bag. Then he went to see the King.

The King was at his table. "And what do you want?" he asked Puss. "Here is a fine rabbit," Puss answered. "It is a gift from the master of the Puss in Boots."

"Tell your master that I thank him," said the King. "It is a very fine rabbit."

The next day, Puss took his bag and went hunting again. He went to another field and lay down in the tall grass.

Two fine fat birds walked by. They, too, smelled the food in the bag, and they walked right inside to get it.

Again, Puss pulled the strings of the bag and went at once to the King's palace.

This time Puss said to the King, "The master of the Puss in Boots sends you these two birds. They are from his fields."

The King was more pleased than ever. "Give my thanks to your master," he said. "And here is some money for you."

Puss made many trips to the palace and took many gifts to the King. One day, while he was at the palace, he heard that the King was going for a ride by the river. He was going with the Princess, who was a very beautiful girl.

Puss ran back to his master. "Today is the day," said Puss. "Do as I say and you will have all you could ever want. This morning you must go for a swim in the river."

While the master was in the water, the King and the Princess passed by.

Puss saw them and shouted, "Help! Help! The master of the Puss in Boots has fallen in the water. Help! Help! He cannot swim!"

The King heard Puss call for help. He quickly told one of his men to pull the master out of the water.

Then Puss said, "A terrible thing has happened. My master's clothes have fallen in the water and now they are lost!"

No one could see that Puss had really picked up the clothes and put them in his bag. They were very old clothes and full of holes, and Puss did not want the King to see his master dressed in them.

"Tell your master I will be glad to give him some of my clothes," said the King. "He has given me so many fine gifts."

Puss helped his master dress in the King's clothes. How fine he looked!

The Princess thought so, too. When she saw the master in his fine new clothes, she fell in love with him at once.

The King, too, was pleased with the way the master looked. He asked the master to ride with him and the Princess.

But Puss ran on ahead. His work was not yet over.

Puss Goes to See the Giant

Puss ran down the road and called to all the farmers he passed, in all the fields, "Hear me well. The King is coming. He will ask to whom the fields belong."

Puss went on. "You must say that the fields belong to the master of the Puss in Boots. If you do not say this, something terrible will happen to you."

The farmers had seen many cats, but they had never seen a cat in boots. They thought Puss must be the greatest cat in the whole world. They were afraid not to do what he said.

The King rode by. "Who owns these beautiful fields?" he asked. The farmers answered as Puss had told them to, "These fields belong to the master of the Puss in Boots."

Of course, Puss knew that the fields really belonged to a terrible giant. And so while the King passed through the fields, Puss ran to the giant's castle.

"Oh, Giant," said Puss, "I hear that you are very clever. I hear that you can do magic tricks. I would like to see one."

"I'll show you," said the Giant. He waved his hand. "Now I will turn into a lion," he said. And, as he said it, he did turn into a lion.

Puss was very much afraid of the lion. But he did not show that he was.

When the Giant changed back to himself, Puss said, "That is a pretty good trick. But I bet you can't turn into a small animal, like a mouse."

This made the Giant angry. "Of course I can!" he shouted.

And as he said it, he turned into a very small mouse.

Quickly, before the giant could change back, Puss ate him up. And that was the end of the Giant.

When the King and the Princess and the master got to the Giant's castle, they found Puss. "Welcome to the castle of the master of Puss in Boots," Puss said.

The master was very surprised, but he said nothing.

"Does this fine, big castle belong to your master, too?" asked the King. "And all the fields around it?"

"Of course," said Puss. "Won't you come in and have dinner with us?"

"Thank you, we will," said the King. He thought how nice it would be if this fine man would marry the Princess.

So after dinner, the King asked the master of Puss in Boots if he would like to marry the Princess.

"This very day, if you please," said the master.

And after they were married, the master and the Princess lived in the castle together with the wonderful Puss in Boots. They were all very happy.

Olaf Mails a Letter

"Olaf," said his mother, "will you mail a letter for me?"

"What will you give me?" Olaf asked.

"Nothing," said his mother. "You should do it because I ask."

"O.K.," said Olaf.

"I will give you a cookie when you get back," said his mother.

"For mailing the letter?" Olaf said.

"No! Because I want you to have a cookie," said his mother.

Olaf went to the corner. There was no mailbox there. But there was a basket. The sign on the basket said *Put Litter Here.*

"I can read," said Olaf. "But they can't spell." He put the letter in the basket.

Olaf ran home and told his mother. "Oh, no, Olaf!" she said. "A litter basket is to throw things away in."

"Oh," said Olaf. "Why didn't the sign say so?"

"It did," said his mother. "Now get the letter and mail it. Eat this cookie on the way."

"O.K.," said Olaf.

There was a truck by the basket. A man was throwing the papers in the truck.

"Stop!" said Olaf.

It was too late. Olaf told the man about the letter.

"I'll help you look," said the man. They looked for the letter.

Some of the papers blew away. Olaf ran after them.

"Here it is!" Olaf said. "Thank you for helping me."

"Glad to help," said the man.

Olaf put the letter in the mailbox. He said, "Why don't they tell us all the words at the same time? Then things like this couldn't happen."

Why Did a Silly?

Why did a Silly throw a clock off the roof?
He wanted to see time fly!

Why did a Silly put his ear next to the tree?
He wanted to hear the tree bark!

Why did a Silly feel sorry for the umbrella?
It was shut up!

The White Bird

Once there was a white bird. The bird lived in a tree in a city park. She slept in the tree at night. In the morning, she flew down into the park to look for things to eat.

In the summer, many people were in the park. They came to the park to eat their lunch.

When they saw the white bird, they said, "Oh, what a beautiful white bird!" And they threw bits of food on the grass for the white bird.

They gave the bird cookie crumbs and bread crumbs and bits of fruit. Sometimes drops of their ice cream fell on the grass, and the white bird had ice cream for lunch.

Different people came to the park every day. They gave the white bird many different things.

But there was one lady who used to come every day to feed the white bird. She was very old.

The lady had a bakery. Every morning she broke the leftover bread into bits.

Then, she took the broken up bread to the park, and put it down on the grass for the white bird to eat.

The people who came to the park called the old lady the Bird Lady.

The Bird Lady was the white bird's best friend. The white bird would come and sit on her arm. Sometimes the white bird would eat from the Bird Lady's hand.

Other people gave food to the white bird, but the bird did not eat from their hands.

The Bird Lady came to the park every day. Even in the cold winter.

In the winter, not many people came to the park. It was too cold to eat lunch in the park.

Only the Bird Lady came to the park every day in the year. She never forgot the white bird. No matter how cold it was, no matter how hard the wind blew, no matter how hard it snowed, the Bird Lady came every day with bread crumbs for the white bird.

If it was very cold, the old lady would have three winter coats on, one over the other. But she always came.

Then one day, in the middle of the winter, the Bird Lady died.

The white bird did not know what had happened to the Bird Lady. The white bird waited every morning for the old lady, but she never came again. And because it was winter, no one else came to the park to feed the white bird.

The white bird looked everywhere for crumbs. But there was not much to eat. The white bird grew very thin.

Then it began to snow. It snowed and snowed. Soon the snow was so deep that the white bird could not walk. She flew from tree to tree in the park, looking for something to eat. But there was nothing there.

Sometimes people walked through the park. They walked by with their heads down. They didn't see the white bird in the trees.

The thin white bird looked for a place where she could get out of the wind and the snow. At last, she saw a window on the top floor of a tall building by the park. There was a window sill where she could sit. The roof of the house came out over the window and kept off the snow.

The white bird flew up to the window. It was very hard for her to fly up so high in the windy snow. She sat near the window, out of the wind. Then a little girl inside the house saw her.

"Mother," she called, "Look! It's the white bird from the park. It's the Bird Lady's bird! She's sitting right on our window sill!"

"Poor thing," said the mother. "She wants to get out of the snow."

"Would she come in?" asked the little girl. "May I let her out of the snow?"

"She would be afraid," said the mother. "But I'm sure she's hungry. You could put some crumbs by the window for her."

The girl ran to get some crumbs. She opened the window.

The white bird was afraid when the window went up, so she flew up to the roof.

Now she was in the wind again. She looked down at the girl's window and saw the crumbs.

The little girl shut the window.

The white bird was still afraid. But she needed food. She flew down quickly and took a crumb. Then she flew off to the park.

The little girl watched from the window. Soon, the white bird flew back to the window and took another crumb.

This time she flew only as far as the roof. Soon she came back.

This time she stayed by the window. She ate all the crumbs that the little girl had put out for her.

The little girl stayed very still, watching the white bird.

The white bird stayed in the corner of the window sill until it stopped snowing. Then she flew off to the park again.

The next day, there was still snow on the ground. There was no food in the park, so the white bird flew back to the girl's window. She found more crumbs there.

Every day the little girl put crumbs on the window sill. She never forgot about the white bird. No matter how cold it was, no matter how hard it snowed, she always put out crumbs for the white bird.

One day the white bird flew to the window just as the little girl was putting out the crumbs. She took a crumb from the little girl's hand. She sat on the little girl's hand to eat the crumb. Then she flew away.

"Mother!" called the little girl. "Mother, the white bird ate from my hand!"

The little girl's mother smiled. "The white bird has a new friend," she said.

So all that winter the little girl put out crumbs for the white bird. When summer came, she went to the park and put crumbs on the grass for the bird.

Now when the white bird saw the little girl coming, she flew right down to her. Sometimes she ate from the girl's hand.

"Look!" people said. "There's the Bird Girl. The white bird always comes to her."

BOSTON

THE THREE BEARS

Part Three

This Small Spot

This small spot is alive!
It moves!
Over my arm
    it goes,
    and stops,
    and goes again.
How can something so small
Be alive?
How does it know
    what to eat,
    where to move,
    when to stop or to go?

Look at it move
Over my hand.
It's alive!
And I can't understand
How something so small
Can know about all
The things it must know—
Can know
    when to move,
    when to stop,
    where to go.
This spot is alive!

The Girl from Mexico

A girl from Mexico had come to live next door to Ann. Her name was Carmen. One day Ann asked her friends to come over to meet Carmen.

"Try to talk slowly to Carmen," said Ann. "She can't talk English very well."

"What does she talk?" asked Ted.

"Spanish," answered Ann. "In Mexico everyone talks Spanish."

"I can say 'Good morning' in Spanish," Bill said. Just then, Carmen came out. She looked at Ann's friends but she didn't say anything.

"Hi, Carmen," Bill said. "*Buenos días*!"

Carmen smiled then. "*Buenos días*," she said.

She came down the steps.

"*Buenos días*," everyone shouted.

But after that, nobody said anything.

"Do you know any more Spanish words?" Ann asked Bill.

"No," Bill answered. "*Buenos días* is all."

"Then we should teach Carmen how to talk English," Ann said.

"How?" Ted asked.

"Like this," Ann said. She looked at Carmen, pointed to herself, and said slowly, "I–am–Ann."

Then Bill pointed to himself. "I–am–Bill," he said.

"I–am–Ted," said Ted.

Carmen laughed.

"*Buenos días*," she said, "I–am–Carmen."

"Right!" said Bill.

The children were all pleased. Teaching English was fun!

“Good for you, Carmen,” said Ted. “Hey kids,” he said to the others. “Let’s take Carmen around the block and teach her the English words for all things we see!”

Ann took Carmen’s hand, and they all went to the fruit store.

“Do you like fruit?” asked Ted, patting his stomach and pointing to the fruit.

“I like fruit,” said Bill.

“I like fruit,” said everyone.

Carmen patted her stomach and smiled. She pointed to the fruit. “I like fruit,” she said.

Then Carmen pointed to a banana. "I like *banana*," she said.

"Banana!" shouted Ted. "We say banana, too!"

"I guess banana is the same in Spanish and English," Bill said. "But they sound a little different."

"Maybe other fruit has the same name, too," said Ted. He pointed to an apple.

"Apple?" he asked Carmen.

But Carmen pointed at the apple and said, "*Manzana.*"

"Well, that's not the same," said Bill. "I can say it. Listen: *Manzana.*"

Everyone smiled and said, "*Manzana.*"

Ann was looking inside the fruit store. She pointed to a cat. "Cat," she said.

Carmen said, "*Gato.*"

"*Gato,*" Carmen said again. Then she said, "Cat?"

"Right!" said Ann. "And look behind her!"

Three kittens were drinking milk from a bowl.

Carmen looked. "*Uno, dos, tres* cats!" she said, pointing to them all.

"Oh, I know, I know. Carmen is counting in Spanish!" said Ted.

"One, two, three *gatos,*" said Ann.

Then Bill said, "*Uno, dos, tres gatos* like milk."

"*Sí,*" Carmen said. "*Leche.* One, two, three cats like *leche!*"

"*Sí* means yes," Ted said, "and *leche* must mean milk."

"Hey, this is good," said Ann. "We're learning Spanish."

Then Bill said, "*Sí, gatos* like *leche.*"

And Carmen said slowly, "*Sí*, cats like milk."

Ann said, "Hey, listen, kids. Carmen is talking English!"

"*Sí, sí,*" Bill said. "Carmen is talking English, and *uno, dos, tres* kids are talking Spanish. This is a *buenos días!*"

"*Sí, sí!*" everyone shouted.

Carmen smiled. "Yes," she said. "Yes, yes, yes!"

The Seal Store

Fred was a boy who loved seals. He loved to look at the seals in the zoo.

He wished he could have one for a pet.

Of course, he didn't get one.

But when he grew up, Fred opened a Seal Store. And now he had seals—a whole store full of them!

Fred put a sign on the front door.

SEAL STORE
SEALS FOR SALE

A little old man and a little old lady came along.

They stopped to look at the sign.

"My word," said the little old lady. "Seals for sale! What will stores sell next?"

The little old man said, "Times have changed all right. Things aren't what they used to be!"

And they both went on their way.

Fred took good care of his seals.

He gave them fish. He made them a place to swim.

He gave them good clean water. Fred talked to his seals. He loved them all, but he knew he couldn't keep all of them.

No one came to buy a seal.

Fred put a bigger sign on the store window.

Along came a boy with his father.

They stopped and looked at the sign.

"A seal!" cried the boy. "Just what I want for my birthday."

But his father said, "No."

"I'm sorry," he said, "but our apartment is too small for a seal."

And they both went on their way.

Days and days and weeks and weeks went by. But no one came to buy a seal.

The seals grew and grew and grew. They got bigger and bigger, and fatter and fatter.

They had baby seals.

Now there were too many seals for Fred's seal store.

So Fred had to move to a bigger store. He made a very big place for the seals to swim. He got trucks full of fish for them. He talked to them.

He loved them all.

But no one came to buy a seal.

Fred put a very big sign on the big door.

A little girl and her mother came along.

They stopped and looked at the sign.

"Mother!" said the little girl. "May I have a seal for a pet?"

The mother said, "A seal for a pet? No! I think a dog would be much better."

And they both went on their way.

The seals climbed all over the big store. They splashed in the water. They barked. Fred gave them more and more fish. He talked to them. He loved them all. But the store was full of seals, and no one came to buy one.

Fred began to teach the seals to do tricks.

He taught them to jump when he said "Go."

He taught them to throw balls.

He taught them to bang drums.

He taught them to climb up little steps.

Now many people came along.

They looked at the sign.

They looked in the window and saw the seals catching balls and jumping into the water.

"Look at the seals!" they said to one another.

Many more people came to watch. They came back day after day to see the seals.

But no one went into the store to buy a seal.

Days and days and weeks and weeks went by.

The seals grew and grew. They got bigger and bigger and fatter and fatter.

The big seals had little seals.

Now there were too many seals, even for the big store.

Fred had to move once more.

This time, he moved the seals outside. He took them to a big park.

He put a sign on the trees.

SEALS FOR SALE

Now the seals did their tricks outside, where everyone could see them.

And everyone came! They all stopped and looked. But still, no one wanted to buy a seal.

One man came up to Fred.

He said, "You have a great show here. Everyone wants to stop and see it. Why don't you make people pay?"

"Pay!" said Fred. "Just to look?"

"Sure!" said the man. "Your seals are wonderful."

So Fred put up a new sign.

And people came.

They were glad to pay money to see the show.

The seals did wonderful tricks. They splashed and barked.

Fred was happy. Now he had a hundred seals, and he didn't even have to sell one!

Barry's Beanbag Game

The Newspaper Story

Mrs. Weeks was reading a newspaper story to her class. It was a story about children in the hospital.

The story said:

> Were you ever in a hospital when you were young?
>
> How did it feel?
>
> Doctors at Park Hospital are asking for money for children's toys. Some children at the hospital must stay in bed for many weeks. Toys are needed to keep these children happy and quiet. Money for them can be sent to the hospital.

After Mrs. Weeks read the story, she said, "This story gave me an idea."

"I know," said one of the boys. "You want us to bring some money for the toys."

"Well, that would be nice," Mrs. Weeks said. "But most third grade children don't have much money. I had another idea."

"I know," said a girl. "We could bring some of our own toys for the children in the hospital."

"That would be nice, too," said Mrs. Weeks, "but that still wasn't what I was thinking."

"I know," said a boy. "We could *make* some toys."

Mrs. Weeks smiled. "Do you think you could?" she asked.

"I couldn't," said one boy. It was a boy named Barry. "I couldn't make anything."

"Bet you could," said one of his friends. "You could make an airplane. Anyone can make planes."

"Not me," Barry said. "I couldn't."

"I'll show you," said his friend. "All you need is some wood."

"I know how to make a good train," said another boy. "My brother showed me. All you need is some shoe boxes."

"Shoe boxes!" said a girl. "You know what I do with shoe boxes? I make doll beds. I just love to make doll beds. I paint the boxes. Then I make covers for the beds. I make the covers from little pieces of cloth. I must have made hundreds of doll beds."

"Well, I'm not going to make doll beds," said Barry.

"Paper dolls!" said another girl. "I can make beautiful paper dolls. I cut them out and paint the faces. Sometimes I make funny faces. Then I make dresses. I can make hundreds of dresses for paper dolls."

"I can make dresses for real dolls," said another girl.

"I can make a toy truck with a spool and a rubber band," said a boy.

"How do you do that?" asked Mrs. Weeks.

"You turn the rubber band around a little stick of wood," said the boy. "Then the truck runs along the floor."

"You'll have to show me," said Mrs. Weeks. "I don't know very much about making trucks."

"I'll show you," said the boy.

"Well," said Mrs. Weeks. "I guess we can make all kinds of things. I'm pleased to find out how much you children know."

"We know how to make hundreds of things," said one of the girls.

"Not me," Barry said. "I couldn't make anything."

Mrs. Weeks asked the class to bring the boxes and cloth and other things they needed to school.

"And I will get some paint and some rubber bands and some string," said Mrs. Weeks. "We'll need those, too."

The next day the third grade began to make toys for the Park Hospital. They brought food cans and pieces of wood. They brought beans and little wheels from old toys.

Everyone brought something — except Barry.

"I couldn't think of anything," he said. "I can't think of anything to make."

The other children thought of lots of things.

Every day after lunch, they worked on their toys. The whole room was full of the sound of their busy work.

Some of the boys were making airplanes out of pieces of wood.

They put wheels on the planes and painted windows on the sides.

"Who's got the paint?"

"Hey, I need some wood."

"Someone took my wheel."

"Mrs. Weeks, I need some help."

Everyone was busy. Except Barry.

The boys showed their planes to him.

"Look, Barry," they said. "Anyone can make a plane."

Barry said, "No, not me. I can't do anything like that."

Barry watched the girls making doll dresses out of cloth. He watched them making dresses out of paper.

"You won't catch me doing that," he said.

The girls showed off their dolls to Barry. They had made big dolls and little dolls, and they had sewed doll dresses out of the cloth they had brought.

"See, Barry," they said. "Dolls are easy."

"Well, I'm not going to make a doll," said Barry.

The Game

Barry watched some of the other children fixing up cans. They took the paper off the cans and painted them. They put little cans inside big cans, and even smaller cans into the little cans.

The cans were for the smaller children at the hospital. The third graders thought smaller children would like to put little cans into bigger ones.

Barry was surprised by all the things his friends were making. Even Mrs. Weeks was surprised.

One boy knew how to make pinwheels. He showed his friends how to pin red and blue paper to a stick. After school they ran around the room with their pinwheels turning.

One day a boy's father brought some big wooden boxes from his store. He helped the boys put wheels on the boxes to make trains.

"Hey," said a boy. "The children in the hospital could put the smaller toys away in the trains."

"Yes," said one of the girls. "And we could paint some boxes to keep toys in, too."

Every day the pile of toys in the back of the room grew bigger. Barry was the only one who didn't make any toys.

Then two girls began to make beanbags. They made little bags out of cloth. They put beans in the bags and sewed them up. Then they threw the beanbags at each other to see how they were. Then—

Barry thought of something to make!

The next day Barry brought a big box to school.

"What is that for?" asked Mrs. Weeks.

"A game," said Barry.

Barry cut holes in the big box. He painted numbers next to the holes. Then he showed the class how the game worked. "Look," he said. "You throw beanbags at the box and try to get them into the holes."

"You try to get a beanbag in the hole with the biggest number," Barry said.

It was a very good game. The third grade called it Barry's Beanbag Game. At lunch time and after school they all wanted to play it.

"I can make millions of beanbag games," Barry said. "I like to make them."

Mrs. Weeks said, "Well, I think we have just about enough toys now. But before we send them to the hospital, I think we should ask the other grades to come and see them."

The third grade put all the toys out on their desks. Then all the children in school came to see them. Even the principal came. The third grade showed the principal how to play Barry's Beanbag Game.

"How did you do it?" asked the principal. "How did you think of so many toys?"

"It wasn't hard," said one of the girls.

"Anyone can make toys," Barry said.

"I couldn't!" said the principal.

All the children laughed.

Then the principal helped the children put the toys into the trains and boxes.

The class took the toys out to the school bus. The bus driver took the toys to the hospital.

A few days later, Mrs. Weeks read another newspaper story to the third grade. This is what it said:

> A school bus brought toys to the Park Hospital this week. The toys were made by the boys and girls of Grade Three in the Green Street School. Doctors at the hospital said, "We have never had so many wonderful toys. Our sick children are very happy with them. Everyone at the hospital says, 'THANK YOU, GRADE THREE!' "

What Came Next?

"I'm hungry," said Pete. "I guess I'll make a sandwich."

So he got out some bread. Then he put some butter on the bread.

"I'm *very* hungry," Pete said. He put some lunch meat on the bread.

And what came next?
Some cheese.

What came next?
Some chicken.

What came next?
Some egg.

What came next?
Some tomatoes.

What came next?
Some beans.

"Oh boy," said Pete. "Now *that's* what I call a sandwich. Well, here I go. I'll eat it." So he did.

And what came next . . . ?
The doctor!

"I Wish I Were an Indian"

"I wish I were an Indian," Ellen said.

Ellen lived in an Indian village, but she was not an Indian. She lived in the village because her father was a teacher in the Indian school.

Ellen was watching the Indian children get ready for Indian Day. "It's a wonderful day," Ellen's friends told her. "We have songs and dances and games, and lots of things to eat."

Ellen's friend, Little Star, was making an Indian dress. "May I help you sew?" asked Ellen.

"Will you, Ellen?" asked Little Star. "If you help me, I can sew my dress much faster."

So Ellen and Little Star cut and sewed the dress.

When they were done, Little Star's dress was beautiful.

Later, Ellen saw Happy Fire making some Indian bread.

"Will you please let me help?" she asked.

"Oh, good, Ellen," said Happy Fire. "I have so much bread to make, I really need some help."

So Ellen helped Happy Fire with the bread. When it was done, Ellen and Happy Fire tried some. It was very good. "Thank you for helping me," said Happy Fire.

Then Ellen saw Dancing Feet making up a new dance.

"Could you teach me your dance?" Ellen asked. "I'd just love to dance with you!"

"Come on!" said Dancing Feet. "I really need someone to dance with."

So Dancing Feet taught Ellen the Indian dance.

At last, Indian Day came. All the Indian children were ready for the fun.

Ellen came along to watch.

"I wish I were an Indian!" Ellen thought to herself again.

Ellen watched Little Star go by in the dress that she had helped to make.

She saw Happy Fire giving out the Indian bread that she had helped to make.

She watched Dancing Feet getting ready to do the dance she had danced with him.

And then, all at once, everyone was quiet. The Indian children all turned to Ellen. Dancing Feet came to her.

"Come and dance, Ellen," he said.

"But I'm not an Indian," Ellen said.

"From now on, you *will* be an Indian!" Dancing Feet told her.

Then the Indian children came to stand in front of Ellen. The chief of the Indian village put his big hand on Ellen's head.

"We make you our Indian sister," he said. "You helped everyone, so your Indian name will be Helping Hand."

"Come and dance, Helping Hand," said Dancing Feet.

So Ellen began to dance with Dancing Feet.

And Little Star and Happy Fire and all the other Indian children stood around them and smiled at their new sister, Helping Hand.

The Fountain in the Park

On Saturdays, Andy liked to go to the park. It was hot and noisy in his house, but the park was always quiet and green. Sometimes Andy would find a boy in the park to play with.

One Saturday, Andy fixed himself a big long sandwich of lunch meat, cheese, tomatoes, and bread.

Then Andy went to the park. He sat under a tree near the drinking fountain and looked around. He saw men reading newspapers and babies sleeping. He saw people walking their dogs. But he didn't see another boy.

After a while, Andy lay down on the ground under the big tree and looked up at the blue summer sky.

Everything was bright in the summer sun. But suddenly Andy felt a drop of water. Then he felt another, right in his face. How could it be raining?

Andy sat up and looked around.

A boy was standing at the drinking fountain, squirting water at Andy.

"What did you want to do that for?" asked Andy, jumping up. Did the boy want to fight, or what?

The boy didn't say anything. But he had his hand on the fountain, and he was laughing.

Andy walked slowly over to the fountain. "Don't squirt me again," he said.

The boy didn't say anything. But when Andy got nearer, the boy squirted him again.

Now Andy was angry. He pushed the boy.

The boy laughed and pushed him back.

"Stop it!" said Andy.

He started to take a drink of water. But just as the water came up, the boy pushed again. The water went in Andy's eye.

"Listen, you'd better stop it," Andy said. Then he went back and sat down with his back against the tree. The boy was laughing at him.

Andy didn't know what to do, so he opened the paper bag. He took out his sandwich and began to eat.

He looked at the other boy while he ate. The boy was watching Andy, but now he wasn't laughing.

Andy ate more of the sandwich.

"You want a drink?" the boy said.

"Come on and get a drink. I won't squirt you this time."

Andy didn't know what to do. The boy was pretty big. Andy didn't want to get in a fight. But he did want some water. He walked over to the fountain again. This time the boy didn't squirt him.

Andy took a long drink. Then he began to show off. He squirted the fountain water this way and that.

"Bet you can't hit that tree," the boy said.

"Bet I can," Andy said. He made the water hit the tree.

"Pretty good," said the boy.

Andy went back to his sandwich. The boy came after him and sat down.

"That looks like a pretty good sandwich," the boy said.

Andy was almost full.

"You want the rest of it?" Andy asked.

"If you don't want it," the boy said.

Andy broke the sandwich and gave a big piece to the boy.

"What's your name?" Andy asked.

"Pete," the boy said.

Pete took one big bite, and then another. Soon, the sandwich was gone.

Then Pete lay back on the grass. He took some baseball cards from his pocket.

"Want to see them?" he asked.

"Sure," said Andy.

The boys looked at Pete's cards. They played together the rest of the day.

On the next Saturday they met in the park again, by the fountain. This time Andy had fixed two sandwiches — one for himself and one for Pete.

"How come you kept squirting me the other day?" Andy asked once while they were eating.

"Oh, I guess I just wanted to make friends," Pete said.

Andy laughed. "That sure was a funny way to go about it," he said.

"Well," said Pete, "it worked."

The Nine-Thousand-Egg Lunch

"Time to get lunch!" says Mrs. March. "But first, I must have nine thousand eggs."

The helpers come running into Mrs. March's big kitchen. They wash up nine thousand eggs, and they get out the big pots to cook them in.

Mrs. March and her helpers put the nine thousand eggs into the pots.

"Good," Mrs. March says. "We'll cook them until they're hard. I need nine thousand hard eggs."

But who will eat nine thousand eggs?

"Next," says Mrs. March, "I must make some soup. Let's see: I need nine thousand carrots, hundreds of potatoes, onions, and tomatoes, and lots of big soup bones."

So Mrs. March's helpers get out nine thousand carrots, hundreds of onions, potatoes, the tomatoes, and lots and lots of big soup bones.

The helpers cut up the carrots. They cut up the onions. They cut up the potatoes.

Mrs. March puts the soup bones into some big soup pots. The helpers put in the carrots and the onions and the potatoes and the tomatoes. Then they fill the pots with water, cover them, and put them on the fire. Now the soup begins to cook.

"Good," says Mrs. March. "It smells like good soup."

But who will eat nine thousand bowls of soup?

"Now," Mrs. March says, "I must make nine thousand cookies."

Mrs. March and her nine helpers put flour and sugar and butter and other good things together in some big bowls. Then they cut out nine thousand sugar cookies, and they bake them until they're done.

Then Mrs. March takes the cookies out. "Yes, they're good sugar cookies," she says.

Nine thousand sugar cookies! Who will eat them all?

"Now," says Mrs. March, "lunch is ready. Come and get it!" she calls.

Then the helpers take the pots of soup and the boxes of eggs and cookies out of the kitchen. Many trucks are waiting outside on the street. The truck drivers and the kitchen helpers put all the food into trucks.

The drivers jump into the trucks and drive away with the food.

Where are they going with nine thousand eggs, nine thousand cookies, and those big pots of soup?

The trucks go all over town. When a truck comes to a school, it stops and the driver takes some of the food into the building.

Then he comes out and drives on to another school.

So all around the city, in all the schools, nine thousand children have soup and eggs and cookies for lunch.

And back in her kitchen, Mrs. March says, "Spaghetti tomorrow!"

A Poem

I have a secret place to go.
Not anyone may know.

And sometimes when the wind is rough
I cannot get there fast enough.

And sometimes when my mother
Is scolding my big brother

My secret place, it seems to me,
Is quite the only place to be.

The Beautiful Black Princess

Once upon a time, in a faraway land, there lived a beautiful black Princess.

The Princess lived in a palace of black glass, and golden lions watched over her.

The Princess was as dark as night, and as beautiful as the evening star. The Princes of seven countries wanted to marry her. But the beautiful black Princess was as clever as she was beautiful. She said she would not marry anyone who could not answer three hard questions.

Many fine Princes rode up to the palace of black glass, seeking to answer the three questions. And many fine Princes rode sadly home again. The beautiful black Princess stood near her golden lions and smiled to herself.

Then one day a poor young man came by. He had no horse and no money.

"Whatever do you want with me?" the Princess asked.

"I have heard of your three questions," said the young man.

"My questions are for Princes," said the Princess. "But if you think you're clever enough to answer them, I might let you try. Do you want to try?"

"Maybe I do, and maybe I don't," the young man said. "Maybe I just came by to see your golden lions."

The young man sat down and began to sing. The golden lions came nearer and nearer to him. At last they lay down next to him.

"Well," said the beautiful black Princess, "you have seen my golden lions. Are you going now?"

"Maybe I am, and maybe I'm not," said the young man. "Maybe I just came by to see your black glass palace."

"Then look at it," said the Princess.

The poor young man walked through the rooms of the palace, with the Princess and the lions behind him.

When he had seen all of the palace, the young man sat down on the black glass steps outside and began to sing some more.

"Well," said the beautiful black Princess. "Now you have seen my palace. Are you going?"

"Maybe I am, and maybe I'm not," the young man said. "Let me hear the three questions. I'll see if I care to answer them."

"One at a time," said the Princess. "The first question is: What is the smallest thing in the world?"

"Oh, that's easy," said the young man.

He put his hand on the head of one of the lions and caught a flea. He held his hand out and showed it to the Princess. "Here it is," he said.

"A flea!" laughed the beautiful black Princess. "Seven fine Princes have given the same answer. You are no different from all the others."

"Wait," said the young man. "I did not say that this flea that you see was the smallest thing in the world. The smallest thing in the world is the flea you cannot see. That flea is on the back of a flea that is on the back of a flea that is on the back of the flea that you see in my hand."

The Princess walked up and down outside her palace of black glass.

"Well," she said at last, "that was a very clever answer."

"What is your second question?" asked the young man.

"The second question is this," said the Princess. "What is the biggest thing in the world?"

"That is easy, too," said the young man. He held out his hand. "The biggest thing in the world is in my hand."

"In your hand!" said the Princess. "But there is nothing in your hand. Nothing at all!"

The young man smiled. "Not so," he said. "There is air on my hand and air all around my hand. There is air over the whole world, so air must be the biggest thing in the world."

"Well," said the Princess, "that is a good answer. Will you try the third question now?"

"I will," said the young man.

"Tell me, then," said the Princess, "what is the most beautiful thing in the world?"

The young man patted the heads of the golden lions and smiled to himself.

"That is easy," he said, "the easiest of all."

The young man picked up a looking glass, and gave it to the beautiful black Princess. She looked in the glass and saw herself.

"There is your answer," he said.

The Princess began to laugh.

"Oh, clever young man," she said, "you are the best one of all. But how can you marry me? The man I marry must be a Prince, and you are just a poor young man."

"That's easy, too," the young man said. "If I marry you, I will be a Prince, the Prince of the glass palace, the master of the golden lions."

So the poor young man won the beautiful black Princess and became her Prince. And some said that the new Prince was even more clever than his Princess.

But not the Prince. He always said that no one could be as clever or as beautiful as the beautiful black Princess.

It's Raining

It's raining.

Rain falls on a city street.
It falls down in a driving sheet.
It wets the house,
It wets the store,
It even wets the river more!
It wets the people, too.
The city is dark in the soft, gray rain.
The city is dark in the rain.

It's raining.

Rain falls down on a country hill.
The fields are wet and dark and still.
Rain wets the grass, it wets the land,
It wets the horses where they stand,
And makes the small birds hide.
The country is dark in the soft, gray
rain.
The country is dark in the rain.

Do You Know?

What coat is wet when you put it on?

A coat of paint!

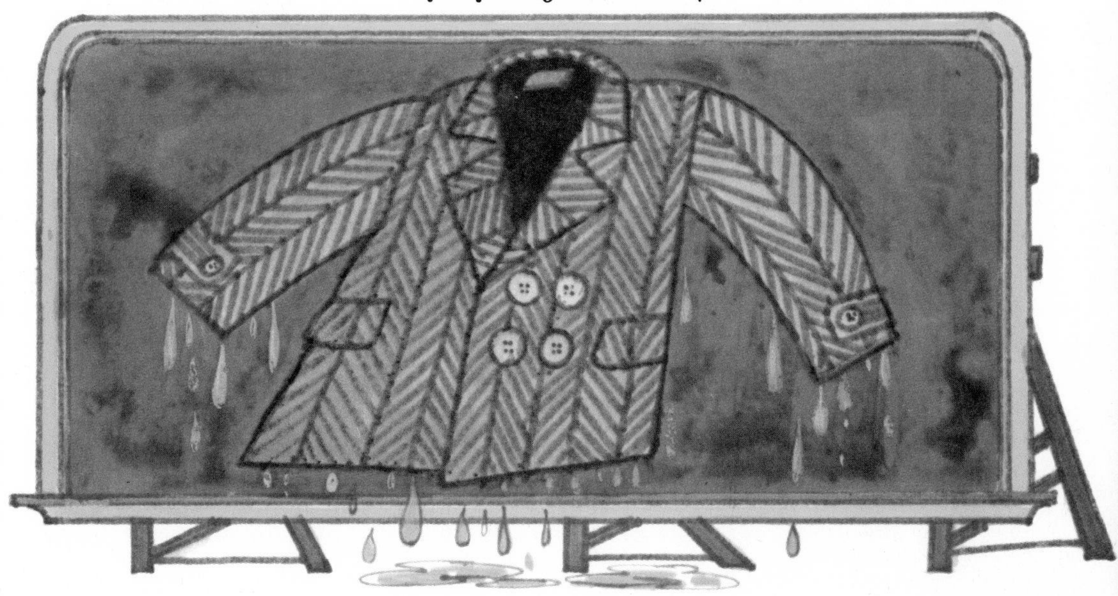

What is the best thing
to put in a cake?

Your teeth!

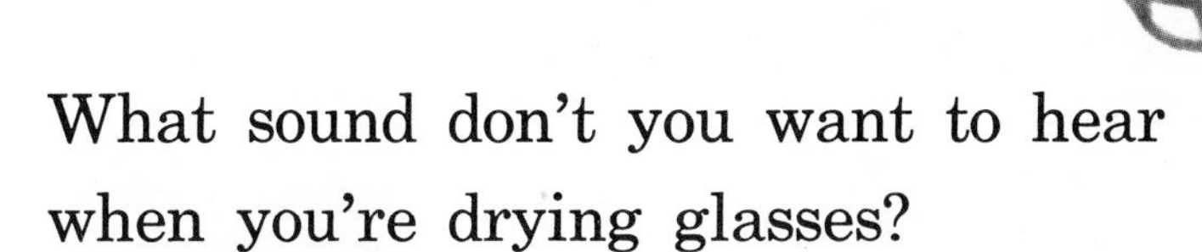

What sound don't you want to hear
when you're drying glasses?

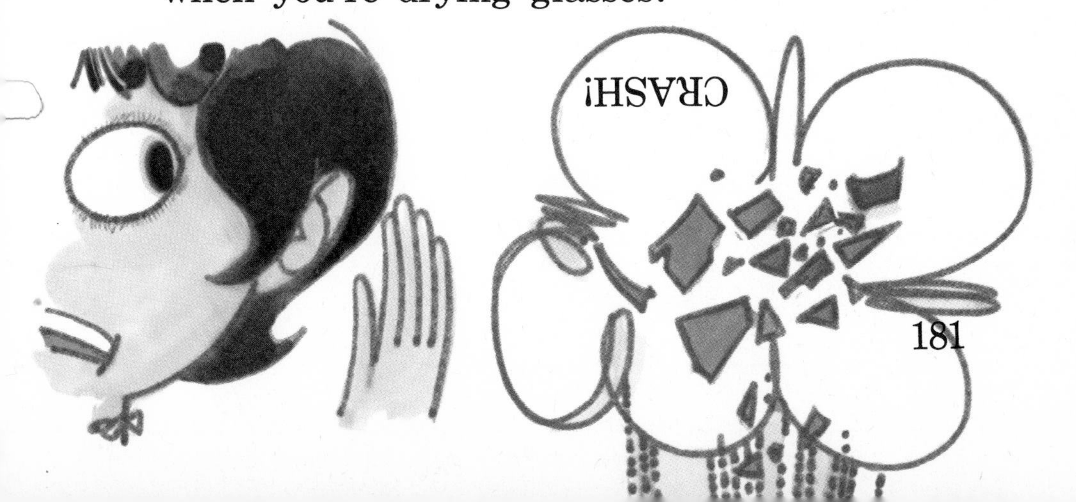

HOUSTON

SEALS

Part Four

Walter's Walkie-Talkie Machine

Walter was a boy who liked to make things.

One day when he was busy working in his room, his mother called, "Walter!"

"Walter!" Walter's mother called again.

Walter did not answer.

"Walter!"

Still no answer.

Walter's mother called as loud as she could, "Walter! Walter!"

Walter looked in the kitchen door. "Did you call me?"

"Call you?" said his mother. "I've been shouting my head off. Why don't you ever answer when I call?"

"I didn't hear you!" Walter said.

"I called and called," his mother said.

"I had the radio on," Walter said. "I couldn't hear you."

"Well, you can now," his mother said. "I want you to go to the store. I need some milk for the baby."

Walter ran to the store for milk. Then he went back to his room.

Then he got out some string and some rubber bands and some old ice cream sticks he had put away. He wanted to make a rocket that would really work.

"Walter!" His mother called again.

But Walter was turning a rubber band tightly around an ice cream stick, and he didn't hear her.

"WALTER!"

Walter kept on working. He didn't hear a thing, he was so busy fixing his rocket.

"WALTER WALKER!"

Walter looked up. Was someone calling his name? He ran to the kitchen. He knew his mother only called his whole name when she was scolding him.

"Did you call me?" Walter asked.

His mother was cleaning up some milk on the floor. Yes, she did look pretty angry.

"I must have called you a million times," his mother said. "If only you'd answer the first time, I wouldn't always have to shout."

"I didn't hear you the first time," Walter said. "I was making a rocket."

"Well, I'm sorry but you'll have to go to the store for me again," said Walter's mother. "The baby spilled all the milk."

Walter ran to the store again and home again.

He gave his mother the milk and ran to his room. He turned on the radio and went back to work on his rocket.

"Walter!"

Walter didn't hear his mother.

"Walter!" she called again.

Walter started his rocket. It flew up!

"WALTER WALKER!"

His mother was standing in the doorway.

"You know what?" said Walter. "My rocket flew!"

"Good for you," his mother said. "Now you fly to the table. We've all been waiting. I've been calling and calling you."

When Walter got to the kitchen, his father was at the table.

"We've been waiting for you," he said. "We could sit here for days before some people hear their mother calling."

"You know," said Walter suddenly, "what we need in this house is a walkie-talkie machine so people can hear each other call."

"You're right," said his father. "And when I make a million dollars, I'll buy one."

"We don't need a million dollars," Walter said. "I can make one for nothing."

Walter's father laughed. "That would be wonderful," he said. "But really, Walter, I don't think a young boy like you can make a walkie-talkie."

Walter ate his dinner and then he asked his mother, "May I have the cans the soup came in?"

"What for?" said his mother.

"You'll see," Walter said.

His mother gave him the cans, and Walter washed them out.

"I need some string, too," Walter said.

His mother got some string for him. Walter took the string and the two soup cans to his room.

Then Walter made a small hole in each can. He put an end of the string through one hole. He made a knot in the end of the string, so it couldn't go back through the hole.

Then he put the other end of the string through the hole in the other can and made another knot. After that he needed one thing more to work with.

"Mother," Walter called.

His mother did not answer.

"MOTHER!"

There was still no answer.

Walter ran to the kitchen. His mother was cleaning up.

"Hey, Mother, I was calling you," said Walter.

"I didn't hear you," his mother said.

"Oh," said Walter. "Well, what I want to know is, do we have any wax?"

"I don't think so," said his mother.

"What about that box of candles we had for the baby's birthday? We only used two of them."

"That's right. The others must be where the string was," said his mother. "What do you need candles for?"

"Wax," said Walter. "May I take three?"

"Why yes," his mother said. "Are they for the rocket?"

"No," Walter said.

Walter ran back to his room with the candles. He used the candles to wax the string between the two soup cans. He pulled the candles along the string until the whole string was waxed.

"Now," said Walter. He put one can down on his bed. He took the other can down to the kitchen, with the string going along the floor behind him. He gave the can to his mother.

"What is that?" his mother asked.

"It's the walkie-talkie machine," said Walter.

"It looks like a soup can with a string in it," his mother said.

"Wait," said Walter. "Just put this can up to your ear and wait. You'll see."

Walter ran back up to his room. He picked up the other can and talked into the open end.

"Hello, hello," he said. "This is Walter talking. Can you hear me? If you can hear me, answer by talking into the can."

Then Walter moved the can to his ear. "Why Walter," he could hear his mother say, "I heard you very well! What a good idea!"

"Good," Walter said. "Now I'll stay up here and work on my rocket. If you need me, just pull on the string and the can in my room will fall over. Then I'll know you want to talk to me, and I'll pick it up and listen."

"Good!" said his mother. "It's a wonderful walkie-talkie, Walter. And it didn't cost a million dollars, either."

Master-of-All-Masters

A Very Old Story

Once a girl got a job taking care of an old man's house.

"Before you begin to work," the old man told the girl, "I should tell you that I have my own names for things, and you must use the same names that I do."

"Very well, sir," said the girl.

"What will you call me?" the old man asked.

"Mr. Snow," said the girl, for that was his name.

"No, no, you must call me Master-of-all-masters," said the old man.

"And what do you call this?" he asked, pointing to his bed.

"I'd call it a bed," said the girl.

"No, no, that's my *night-right*," said the old man.

Then he pointed to an old suit of clothes. "What is that?" he asked.

"That's an old suit," said the girl.

"No, no, that's my *keep-warm*," said the old man.

"And what is this?" he asked, pointing to his cat.

"A cat," said the girl.

"You must call my cat *Fur-on-four-feet*," said the man.

Then he pointed to the fire. "What's this?" he asked.

"Fire," said the girl. "Everyone knows that."

"Well, *you* must call it *red-hot-ribbons*," the man told her.

"Now tell me what this is," he said, pointing to some water.

"That's water," the girl said.

"No," said the man, "It's *drink-and-splash*."

"And what is this?" the man asked, pointing all around his house.

"It's your house," said the girl.

"Oh, no," the man said. "You must call it *doors-and-floors*."

That night, after the old man had gone to sleep, the cat got too near the fire. A spark fell on the cat's tail. The cat ran past some paper and the paper caught on fire.

The girl caught the cat and put out the spark. But she could not put out the fire in the paper.

So she called out, "Master-of-all-masters, get out of your night-right and put on your keep-warm. Fur-on-four-feet got a spark of red-hot-ribbons on her tail and unless you get some drink-and-splash, the doors-and-floors will all be red-hot-ribbons!"

The Caterpillars in Our Class

Once we had twenty caterpillar eggs. We had them in a cage in our room. We had them two days. The first egg hatched on a Friday. Only Rosemary saw the eggs hatch—because she was the last one to go home that day.

Rosemary asked our teacher, "May I look at the eggs one more time before I go home?" And when she went to the cage, she didn't see twenty eggs. There were twelve eggs and eight tiny caterpillars there! They had feelers on the top of their heads.

Of course, no one was at school on Saturday and Sunday.

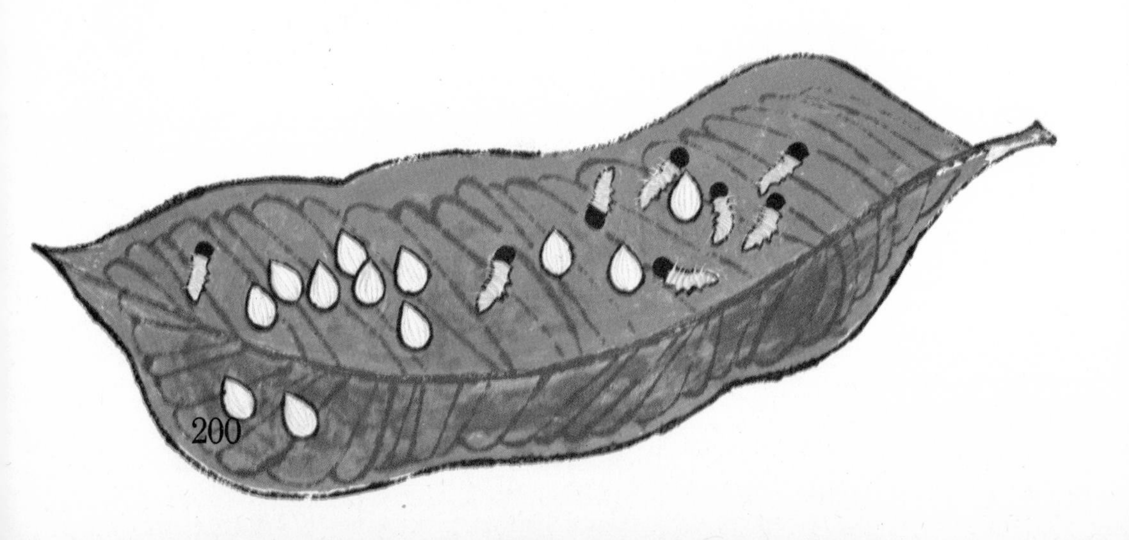

On Monday there were a lot more caterpillars. We all saw them. The caterpillars were light green. They were very small.

The caterpillars changed colors when they were seven days old. Then they were black and white.

The caterpillars got bigger and fatter. We had to find a plant called milkweed for them to eat. Milkweed is not easy to find in the city where we live. But we found some. The caterpillars ate a lot of it. They were growing very fast.

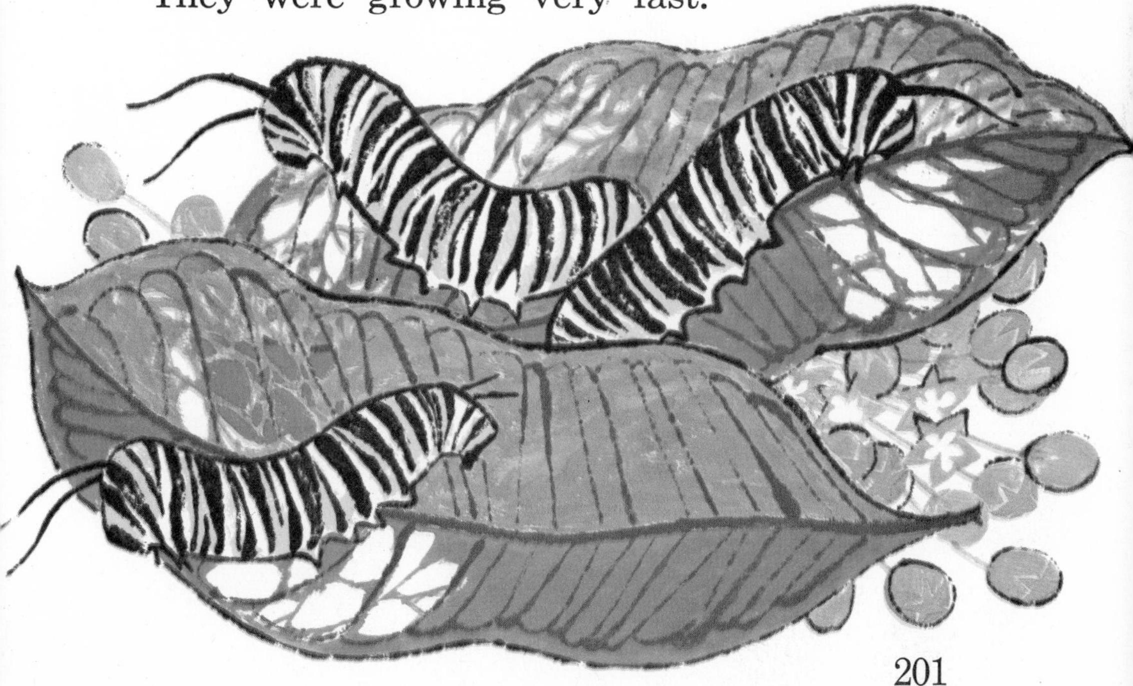

We watched them carefully because we knew that each caterpillar would turn into a chrysalis. After that, a butterfly would come out. Two weeks went by, but not one of the caterpillars had turned into a chrysalis yet.

At last, after three weeks and four days, seven of them did turn into chrysalises! Then another one turned, and we had eight. That was all we had, because one of the caterpillars died and some others got lost.

The chrysalises looked like green wax, and they had spots on them. Inside of each chrysalis, a caterpillar was turning into a butterfly. We could hardly wait to see them come out.

We watched and watched the chrysalises. They changed from just green to blue-green. We could not see inside. But we knew that the butterflies were getting ready to come out.

Suddenly, one day we could see a butterfly wing through one of the chrysalises! That same day, the first butterfly came out.

It was orange and black.

On the very next day, we watched three more orange and black butterflies come out. First they put their back legs out. Then the chrysalises started to crack and break. The cracks got bigger and the butterflies came out.

At first their wings were wet. But soon the butterflies began to move them, and the air made them dry.

After a while, one butterfly flew up to the top of the cage. They all looked very beautiful. We liked to watch them.

One day a lady from the museum came to our class. Her name was Miss Gray. She told us many things about butterflies. She showed us how to feed our butterflies.

Miss Gray also told us how the museum people learn about butterflies. They put numbers on the butterflies and let the butterflies go free. Far away, some other museum people may see the same butterflies. When they see the numbers, they can tell where the butterflies came from.

Miss Gray put numbers on our four butterflies. Doing this is called banding. If a butterfly has a number on it, you say it is "banded."

The next day, more butterflies hatched. One by one, the other butterflies came out. We had butterflies for a whole week!

Then, one day, four of the banded butterflies flew out of the window. They flew out when we were feeding them. In a way that was lucky, because the other butterflies died soon.

We thought maybe they hadn't had enough food. Or that maybe it was too hot in our room. Maybe it is too hard for butterflies to grow up in a school.

Anyway, we said we were lucky about some things!

We were lucky that the eggs hatched.

We were lucky that the caterpillars turned into chrysalises.

We were lucky that the butterflies came out.

And we were really lucky that the butterflies that flew out the window were banded.

Harry the Hero

Harry liked to do things to help people.

He wanted to be like the boys in books who were always good and always helped people.

Harry thought his name could be Harry the Hero.

And when he came to help people, he could say: "Never fear, Harry's here."

One day, Harry put on his cowboy hat and his baseball mitt, just for good luck.

He told his little brother Danny, "I'm Harry the Hero. I'm going out to help people."

"Let me come?" asked Danny.

"Sure," said Harry. So Harry the Hero and his small helper Danny went down the street.

"Listen!" said Harry.

"HELP! HELP! PLEASE HELP!" someone called.

"What's the matter?" asked Harry the Hero. "Does someone need help?"

Danny ran as fast as he could after Harry the Hero.

They found a little girl crying.

"How can I ever get her?" she cried.

"What's the matter, Miss?" said Harry the Hero.

"Look," said the little girl, pointing up at a tree. "My cat got up there, and she can't get down. She's afraid. And I'm afraid she'll fall."

Harry the Hero patted the little girl's head.

"Never fear. Harry's here," he said. "I'll save your cat."

"Don't cry. Your cat will be safe," said Danny. "Harry's here. He will get her for you."

Harry the Hero climbed right up the big tree where the cat was.

"Never fear," Harry the Hero said to the cat. "Harry's here."

The cat did not seem to understand. "Sssst! Sssst!" she said.

Harry took off his big cowboy hat and put it under the cat. Then he pushed the cat just a little.

The cat was afraid. Her claws went out. But Harry had on his baseball mitt, so he didn't feel the cat's claws. He pushed the cat into his hat, and climbed quickly down the tree.

"Oh, thank you, Harry," said the little girl.

"I told you Harry could help you," said Danny.

"It was nothing, Miss," said Harry the Hero. "Never fear when Harry's here. Come on, Danny. Let's get going."

And off down the street went Harry the Hero, with little Danny running after him. After a while, they heard another call.

"HELP! HELP!"

"Come on!" shouted Harry. "Someone needs help."

"I'm coming," said Danny. "As fast as I can."

Down at the corner they saw the lady who had called. She had two big bags of food and they were falling out of her arms.

"HELP! HELP!" she called.

"I'm coming, Lady," called Harry the Hero.

But before he could get to the lady, one of her bags broke. All kinds of fruit fell and rolled down the sidewalk.

The lady looked as if she might cry.

"Never fear, Harry's here," said Harry the Hero. "I'll pick up your fruit."

"Don't cry," said Danny. "Harry's here."

Harry ran after the rolling fruit. He caught them up in his baseball mitt and he put them into his cowboy hat. He caught everything except one apple. That one rolled into the street and got lost under a car.

"Sorry, I was too late to get that one," said Harry the Hero.

"But you got all the others!" said the lady. "You're wonderful!"

"Never fear when Harry's here," said Danny.

"But my bag is broken," said the lady. "How can I carry these things home?"

"I'll carry them in my hat," said Harry.

Harry carried everything home for the lady, except the bread. Little Danny carried the bread, running along behind Harry the Hero, trying to keep up.

"Thank you, boys," said the lady.

"That's all right," said Harry. "Come on, Danny. Let's get going."

And off down the street went Harry the Hero with his cowboy hat and his baseball mitt.

Little Danny came behind.

"HELP! CATCH IT! THROW IT BACK!"

Someone's baseball was rolling down the street. There was an open manhole at the end of the street! Harry the Hero ran over and caught the ball just in time. He threw it back. Then Danny came running up, and he and Harry went on down the street.

"HELP! PLEASE! CATCH IT!"

Harry the Hero looked up. A baby was at the window, crying. The baby's mother was pointing to a teddy bear that had fallen out the window.

Harry picked up the bear. He ran up the steps to the third floor to give it to the baby's mother. His little brother Danny ran after him as fast as he could.

"Thank you, Harry," everyone said.

"Thank you, Harry."

"Thank you, Harry."

"It's nothing," said Harry the Hero. "Never fear, when Harry's here."

And on he went, being a hero. But at last Danny said, "Harry, it's too hard helping you to be a hero. My legs can't go any more."

"Never fear. Harry's here," said Harry the Hero. "Climb on my back. I'll carry you home."

And he did.

"Where have you boys been?" said Harry's father. "You're late."

"Never fear. Harry's here," said Harry the Hero. "And so is Danny."

A Pocketful of Pigs

Once there was no money.

If people wanted to get something, they had to give something. This is the way it used to be.

"I will give you my cow for your pig," a man would say.

"I'll give you my bowl if you give me a shirt," another would say.

"Here are seven oranges for one fish."

"Will you give me a chicken for a bag of corn?"

People had to trade things every day. They had to give a thing to get a thing because there wasn't any money.

But they had to work out a good trade, one that came out even.

What could you get for two chickens? Were three bags of apples a good trade for two bags of grapes? Or one bag of apples for a little butter? What was an even trade? It was hard to know.

And it was too hard to carry around all the things for trading. People had to use too much time getting things they needed. So they thought of a new way to trade.

They thought of money.

Money could "stand for" apples or bowls or pigs.

And a pocketful of money was better than a pocketful of pigs!

With money, it was not so hard to trade. Everyone could use money. The man who needed a pig could buy it with money. The man who sold the pig could keep the money until he needed something. People could work for money, and people could buy things with the money they got from work.

That is how it was, and that is how it is now.

Who Needs Money?

Everyone needs money.

Sometimes children need money but they don't know how to get it. Here are some good ways to make money.

Returning Bottles to Stores

Keep your eyes open for empty soft-drink bottles. Stores that sell soft drinks will pay for many kinds of empty bottles. But look at each bottle carefully. Some bottles say *No Return*. Stores do not pay for this kind of bottle.

Shoveling Snow

After a big snow, sidewalks must be shoveled. Sometimes store men do not have time to do this. They are glad to pay someone to shovel the snow off the sidewalk by the store. Two friends working together can shovel a lot of snow quickly.

Taking Care of Small Children

Mothers with two or three small children sometimes need help. Many mothers would pay a few cents if you would play with their children while they work in another part of the house. You might play games, draw pictures, or read a story to the children.

Mailing Letters

Letter boxes are sometimes a block or two away. Older people and busy mothers may not be able to get out to mail letters. They may be glad to pay you a few cents to mail their letters.

Walking Dogs

Dogs must be walked. Find out which people on your block have dogs. Let them know that for a nickel or two you will walk their dogs. You can take two or three dogs out at the same time — if the dogs like each other!

Helping Older People

If you live in an apartment house, find out if there are any older people in your building. Let them know you will go out for them. Perhaps they will pay you something every week to get their mail or go to the corner store for them.

Helping People Clean Up

People often need help with clean-up work. Tell everyone that you are ready to help with house cleaning and carrying things away. You might carry out piles of old newspapers from someone's closet. You might even sell the old papers!

Carrying Out Garbage

In many buildings, garbage must be taken outside and put in garbage cans. Is this true where you live? If it is, some people might pay you to stop by their apartments each day and take out their garbage for them.

Carrying Bags

When a mother has small children with her, it is sometimes hard for her to carry bags home from the store. You could carry things for her. Maybe you have a wagon or a box on wheels that you could put the bags in. Then you could carry lots of things for people.

There are many ways to make money. Look around you to see what work you can do.

But remember, whatever the work is, be sure to do it well. Show people that you are a good worker. Soon you will not have to look for work. People will look for you!

Benjamin, Benjamin

There was a boy named Benjamin. Whenever he met someone new, he said, "Hello, my name is Benjamin."

One day a new boy came to live on Benjamin's street.

"Hello," said Benjamin. "My name is Benjamin."

The new boy looked at Benjamin.

"My name is Benjamin, too," he said.

"You're a Benjamin, too? How will we know which is which?" said Benjamin.

"I have a second name," said the new boy. "My middle name is John."

"I have a middle name, too," said Benjamin. "My middle name is David. From now on let's both use our first *and* middle names. I will call myself Benjamin David and you call yourself Benjamin John. Then everyone will know which is which."

"O.K., Benjamin David," said Benjamin John. "Good-by now."

"So long, Benjamin John," said Benjamin David. After that, whenever Benjamin David met someone new, he said, "Hello, my name is Benjamin David."

But one day at school, another new boy said, "That's funny. My name is Benjamin David, too."

"You're a Benjamin David, too?" asked Benjamin David. "Now how will we tell which is which?"

"Well, we don't look alike," said the new Benjamin David. "And we don't live in the same house."

"And your mother and father aren't my mother and father," said Benjamin David.

"Your last names are different," said the teacher. "Use them, and then I can tell which Benjamin is which."

After that, when Benjamin met someone new, he said, "My name is Benjamin David Hill."

Then one day, Benjamin David Hill met someone he had wanted to meet for a long time. Benjamin David Hill took a train, then a plane and went out west to meet his grandfather.

His grandfather was waiting at the airport for him.

"Hello! Hi!" called Benjamin. "My name is Benjamin David Hill."

His grandfather smiled.

"That's my name, too," he said. "What do you know about that!"

"Another Benjamin David Hill?" asked Benjamin. "How will anyone ever tell which is which?"

Benjamin's grandfather laughed.

"Well," he said, "I think most people could tell by looking at us. But the best thing would be to tell them where you come from. From now on I will say, 'I am Benjamin David Hill of River Street, New City, California.' "

"And I will say that I am Benjamin David Hill of Park Street, Watertown, New York," said Benjamin.

And that is just what he did.

Old Man Fiddler

Once upon a time, far up in the high hills, there lived an old man called Old Man Fiddler. Old Man Fiddler was very good at playing the fiddle, but he was not very good at anything else.

If Old Man Fiddler went fishing, he would play his fiddle till the fish in the river danced. Old Man Fiddler could make the fish jump around, but he never did catch one for his supper.

If he went to get the cows, Old Man Fiddler played his fiddle so well the cows danced in the fields. But Old Man Fiddler would forget to bring them home.

Old Man Fiddler didn't care. He just liked to be happy with his fiddle.

One day, it was raining very, very hard. But Old Man Fiddler didn't care. He sat in his house, happy as could be, and played away sweet and loud.

As Old Man Fiddler played, a traveler rode by and asked if he could come in to get out of the rain.

"Come in, come in," said Old Man Fiddler, and he went on playing.

After a minute, the traveler saw that there was a hole in Old Man Fiddler's roof, and the rain was coming through.

"Excuse me, sir," said the traveler, "but the rain is coming right in through your roof."

"If you're getting wet, just move over to a dry place," said Old Man Fiddler as he went on playing.

"It doesn't matter to me, sir," the traveler said. "I'm only staying for a little while. But don't you think you should fix your roof? You have to live here."

"Fix my roof?" said Old Man Fiddler. He was so surprised that he put his fiddle down for a moment.

"What do you mean, fix my roof?" he went on. "Can't you see it's raining? Do you want me to go out there and catch a cold, just to fix my roof?" He picked up his fiddle and went on with his playing.

After a while the traveler spoke again. "Excuse me, sir," he said, "but I didn't mean that you should fix it right now."

"Well, then, what did you mean?" asked Old Man Fiddler.

"I was only thinking, sir," the traveler said, "that on some nice day, when the sun is shining and it isn't raining at all, you could go up and fix the roof."

"Get along with you," said Old Man Fiddler. "What a silly idea you have. Why should I fix my roof on a sunny day? When it isn't raining, no rain comes in. Not one little drop!"

And with these words, Old Man Fiddler chased the traveler out of the house and down the road.

Then he went back into the house, picked up his fiddle, and began to play once more.

"Some people are very, very silly," Old Man Fiddler said to himself, as he played his fiddle.

Old Man Fiddler played high notes and he played low notes. He played until the birds came in out of the rain to sing along with him.

People could say what they wanted about his roof.

But when it came to playing the fiddle, everyone had to say that Old Man Fiddler could play better than any man alive.

Lost in the Jungle

We were lost!

Steve and I were looking at a big snake high up in a tree. But Steve turned around suddenly to say, "Hey, where are the other boys?"

I looked around. No one was there.

"They're gone," Steve said. "We're lost! What a place to be lost!" He sounded scared.

Until Steve and I got lost, it had been a good trip. We had walked and walked. We had seen all kinds of animals and birds and snakes that we had never seen before.

Our leader had told us to stay near him. We had never been here before, but our leader knew the way.

He took us to a place where we saw deer eating. After that, he took us deep in the jungle. We saw many monkeys in the trees. Then we came to an open place where there were birds as tall as people.

And then I saw that giant snake. Steve and I stopped to look at the snake. The others went on, and we didn't see which way they went. Now the two of us were alone!

"Which way do you think they went?" Steve asked.

Up ahead, there was a turn. I ran up to look around it. But no one was there.

Steve ran back the way we had come. But he didn't see anyone.

"Over that way, maybe," I said. I was looking at some big rocks.

We ran toward the rocks.

"YEOW!" Steve shouted. He turned back.

A big tiger was behind the rocks! A mean-looking tiger. He looked ready to jump.

"Come on!" I yelled. "I'm scared! Let's get out of here."

We ran the other way. We ran on and on.

At last we stopped to rest.

"That was the biggest tiger I ever saw," Steve said.

"He wasn't after us," I said. "He was after a giraffe. I saw the giraffe."

"We have to find the others soon," Steve said. "It's getting late."

"I know," I said. "But let's rest for a second."

We sat down. We were looking out on a quiet grassy place. Far away, we could see a giraffe eating leaves from a tall tree.

"I'm getting hungry," Steve said.

I had a banana in my pocket. I gave it to Steve.

"Maybe we should save some," Steve said. "What if we don't find the others tonight? This is all the food we have."

"We've got to find the others," I said. "We can't stay here all night."

We began to look again. We kept on going. We got more and more scared.

Once I thought I heard shouts off to the right. We ran that way and almost ran into an elephant.

The elephant was just standing there. Near him were the bones of some big animal.

I didn't like the looks of those bones.

We ran on.

"I'm thirsty," Steve said at last. "I've got to have some water."

I was thirsty, too. We began to look for water.

We pushed on. And then, just as I thought I couldn't stand it any more, we heard a soft sound. "I hear water," I said.

"I hear something else," said Steve. "I hear people!" We ran to the noise.

There was a water fountain, and there were the other boys with our leader. They were all getting a drink. Our scout leader was looking all around.

Our scout leader saw us. "Hey," he said, "where have you been? We were looking all over for you."

"We were lost!" I said.

"Lost in the jungle!" said Steve. "It was terrible. We saw a giant tiger and an elephant and a snake and all kinds of terrible things!"

"Well, I'm glad you got here," said our scout leader. "But after this, you stick with the others, or I'll never take you scouts on a trip to the Museum of Natural History again."

Except Rachel

One day Charles came home from school. "I'm the best runner in my class," he told his mother.

"Except Rachel," he added.

"I caught more hits than anyone today!" said Charles the next time.

"Except Rachel," he said.

"I got the most runs today," Charles said, another day. "Except Rachel," he added.

"Good for you, Charles," said his mother. "But who is this Rachel?"

"Oh, just a girl in our class," Charles said.

One day Charles ran home.

"Hey, Mom!" he said. "I'm captain of the boys' baseball team! We have all the good players."

"What about Rachel?" asked his mother.

"We have all the good players *except* Rachel," Charles said. "Rachel's the captain of the girls' team."

"Boy, are those girls terrible ball players!" Charles said the next day.

"Except Rachel," he added.

"Did your team play their team?" Charles' mother asked.

"Yes," said Charles. "We got two runs. Not one girl got a hit, except Rachel. Their team was terrible. But they won. Rachel made three runs."

"Guess what!" Charles yelled on another day. "Our grade is going to play the third grade. And I'm captain again! Maybe we can win. We have all the good players in the class."

"Except Rachel?" asked his mother.

"Well, yes, except Rachel," Charles said. "We think we should just have boys."

"Oh," said his mother.

On the day of the big game, Charles rushed home. "Mom!" he said. "We won!"

"Wonderful!" said his mother.

"Guess what," Charles said. "Our pitcher wasn't at school today. We had no one to pitch. Except Rachel."

"What happened?" Charles' mother asked.

"The third grade kids laughed at us. They said we must be terrible if we had to have a girl pitcher."

"How did Rachel do?" asked Charles' mother.

"She pitched O.K. But they got two runs off her. Our team felt terrible. But then we got some hits, and Rachel brought them in with a home run! So we won!" said Charles. "Everyone was cheering."

"Wonderful!" said Charles' mother.

"That Rachel!" said Charles. "I really don't like girls very much," he said.

"Except Rachel," he added.

Night Cat

Mac is a fat gray cat.

"A fat, gray, lazy cat," says the boy who lives with Mac.

When the boy gets up in the morning, there is Mac, still sleeping. When the boy gets home from school, there is Mac, still sleeping.

A fat gray lazy cat, sleeping all evening.

"The laziest cat in the world," says the boy.

Still sleeping, until everyone in the house is asleep.

But then—things are different!

The fat gray cat opens his eyes. His two green eyes look all around.

Mac wakes up!

On soft, sure feet, the gray cat goes to the window. Then he goes out of the window and down the fire escape.

Two green eyes look into every corner of the small back yard.

The eyes find a yellow cat and a white cat. Two cats are waiting for Mac.

Now there are three cats in the small yard. They quietly make soft cat sounds.

Six green eyes wait in the dark.

They hear something.

Another cat! A new cat is coming into Mac's back yard.

A tiger cat. A big tiger cat.

Mac and the yellow cat jump onto the fence.

"Sssssst!" says the white cat.

"Sssssst!" says the tiger.

Four cats are fighting! "Sssssst!"

They chase around the yard.

White cat, yellow cat, gray cat, and a tiger cat all fight together.

It is a very good cat fight. After it, the cats are friends. They sit on the fence and lick their fur.

Now it's time for a little night song.

ME–OWWWWWWW—OW—OW—OW! A song for the sleeping city.

A window bangs open. Someone throws a shoe out of the window. The cats go running.

Here comes a dog.

"Grrrrrrrr!" and "Sssssst!"

The cats race away.

Mac gets away first. He runs right by a policeman.

"Hi, cats," the policeman says. "Hi there, Mac."

The cats run on.

Mac sees a garbage can. He jumps on it. So do the others.

Mac finds a fish head deep in the garbage can. Tiger finds a fish tail. Yellow cat and white cat are fighting over some bones.

Four cats have dinner on a garbage can, while the city is sleeping. Everything is very quiet.

Then — EEEEEEEEEEEE!

A fire engine! Four fire engines rush down the street.

The four cats run. They jump up a tree.

Four cats climb high in the tree.

Mac is the first to the top of the tree. The big gray night cat is in the very top of the tree.

The night is almost over. Soon the sun will come up.

It is time for Mac to go.

Good-by to the white cat. Good-by to the yellow cat. Good-by, new friend Tiger.

Mac climbs down the tree. He climbs up the fire escape.

He jumps through the window and he goes back to sleep.

The boy gets up in the morning, and there is Mac, sleeping.

"That lazy cat," says the boy. "That lazy Mac!"

But the fat gray cat doesn't hear a word. Now, in the daytime, he is really the laziest cat in the world.

What If?

What if . . .
you had some magic paint,
so everything you painted
turned real?
What would you paint?

What if . . .
you could be a bird
or a bear
or a crocodile?
What would you be?

What if . . .
you had three wishes
that would all come true?
What would you wish for?

Soft Grass

The sidewalk is hard
Beneath my feet.
Hard, hot sidewalk,
Hard, hot street.

Stony sidewalk,
Stony yard,
Stony buildings,
Hot and hard.

But I go to the park
Along my street,
Where the grass is soft
Beneath my feet.

Off the sidewalk,
Out of the sun,
Over the cool, soft grass
I run!

WASHINGTON D.C.

Vocabulary List

The new words introduced in *Green Light, Go!* are listed below. The number indicates the text page on which a word first appears. Variant forms of words introduced earlier are followed by an asterisk. A word introduced in a compound or in an inflected form is considered a variant when it appears later in the text as a root word. Words that represent sounds and Spanish words are in italics.

10. different
    names*
    hair
    brown
    both
11. Joe's*
12. jumping*
    rope
    front
    inquire
    within*
    turning*
13. —
14. rolling*
15. —
16. older*
    hop
    hopped*
    hopping*
    bumped
    show-off*
17. —
18. handed*
19. quite
    used
    unhappy*
20. cage
21. kitten
    kittens*
    woman's*
    purred*
    mewed
    mew*
    idea
22. —
23. giving*
    hug
    penny
    candy
24. —
25. children's*
    shouting*
    blew
    music
26. middle
    broke
    broken*
    sorry
27. tape
    which
    cares*
28. shut
29. papers*
    Billy's*
    flew
30. Mike
    melted
    snows*
31. Dave
    Sunday
    Saturdays*
    Sundays*
    best
    yesterday
32. wonderful
    cleaned*
    starting
33. bet
    walk*
34. popcorn
35. lions*
    foxes*
    climbing*
    cages*
36. splashed*
    lamb
    deer
    eight
    driver*
    driving*
37. kitchen
    tomatoes
    seconds*
    hearing*
    telling*
38. Bob's
    luck
    Bob*
    radio
    cheering
    shopping
    laundry
39. radios*
40. passed
    bakery
    roar*
41. pow
    I've*
    kid
42. kids*
    Lucky*
43. —
44. ox
45. war
    sweet
    fruit
    crocodiles
    heads*
46. crocodile*
    rushed*
    stick
    crocodile's*
    mouth
    leg*
    Deer's*
    floating
    log
    answer

47. float*
48. sticking*
49. King
sent*
number
counted*
ones*
50. kinds*
51. —
52. pox
mumps
Charlie*
bumps*
lumps
53. note
Charlie's*
itch
scratch
54. —
55. —
56. fine
57. —
58. thunder
lightning
flashes
59. fall*
spring
60. —
61. Denver
62. —
63. —
64. scare*
Donna
Donna's*
65. scared*
creaky
66. held
father's*
tightly
witch
skeleton
67. either
whole
68. giraffe
69. elephant
wouldn't*
70. ant
germ
start*
71. sale
puppies*
72. pointed
licked
lick*
73. waved
softly*
lady
74. twelve
dollars
75. love
shop*
76. pointing*
sell
should
selling*
77. buying*
78. —
79. twenty
80. basket
drove
rang
81. Grandpa
82. squeaky
sneakers
Steve
shoes
sneak*
Steve's*
sneaky*
squeak*
83. —
84. cake
baked*
85. seek
closet
86. —
87. Middletown*
keeper*
hunters*
trap
banana
string
picks*
88. bang
nearby*
caught
89. bananas*
welcome
begin
babies*
island
answers*
90. —
91. —
92. bears*
sends*
93. use*
94. Maria
listen
break
Goldilocks
95. upside*
breaking*
bear's*
chair
96. —
97. Puss
boots
master
oldest*
98. hunting*
lay
pretended
rabbit
strings*
99. gift
fat
100. King's*
palace
pleased*
trips*
101. —
102. master's*
given*
gifts*
103. farmers*
whom
belong
greatest*
rode
owns*
course
belonged*
giant's*
104. clever
105. —
106. marry
married*
107. Olaf
mails*
mailing*
litter
108. throw
throwing*

109. happen*
110. umbrella
111. bits*
112. feed
leftover*
bird's*
lady's
113. matter
114. thin
deep
115. top
sill
116. —
117. snowing*
ground
118. putting*
119. —
120. Boston
121. —
122. —
123. —
124. spot
alive
moves*
125. —
126. Mexico
meet
Spanish
buenos
días
127. teaching*
128. patting*
stomach
129. *manzana*
130. *gato*
uno
dos
tres
counting*
sí
leche
131. means*
132. seal
loved*
seals*
133. —
134. fatter*
Fred's*
135. climbed*
taught
136. —
137. —
138. —
139. hundred
140. Barry's
beanbag*
hospital
young
doctors
asking*
141. —
142. Barry*
wood
shoe*
doll
beds*
cloth
covers
hundreds*
143. dolls*
cut
dresses*
spool
rubber
band
144. bands*
brought
except
145. sides*
who's*
146. sewed
easy
147. fixing
graders*
148. pinwheels
pin*
wooden*
beanbags*
149. numbers*
150. millions
grades*
151. —
152. —
153. butter
154. doctor*
155. Indian
village
Ellen's*
songs*
dances*
sew*
156. star's*
157. Dancing
dance*
158. danced*
159. chief
160. Andy
fixed*
161. suddenly
squirting
squirt*
162. squirted*
Andy's*
eye*
163. —
164. piece*
cards
165. met
166. thousand
helpers*
March's*
cook*
soup
carrots
onions
bones*
167. fill
cover*
begins*
smells*
bowls*
168. flour
sugar
bake*
169. spaghetti
170. poem
secret
rough
scolding
seems
171. evening
Princes*
countries*
questions
172. seeking*
sadly*
whatever*
173. —
174. flea

175. —
176. —
177. easiest*
178. won
179. sheet
wets*
gray
180. —
181. drying*
crash
182. Houston
183. —
184. —
185. —
186. Walter's
walkie-talkie
Walter*
loud
187. sticks*
rocket
188. Walker*
cleaning*
189. shout*
million*
spilled
190. we've*
been
191. —
192. knot
193. wax
candles
baby's*
194. waxed*
195. cost
196. sir
197. masters*
suit*
198. fur
ribbons*
spark
past
199. unless
200. caterpillars
caterpillar*
hatched
Friday
hatch*
feelers*
201. Monday
colors
plant*
milkweed*
202. carefully*
chrysalis
butterfly
chrysalises*
spots*
hardly*
203. butterflies
wing
orange
204. crack*
wings*
205. banding*
banded*
feeding*
hadn't*
206. —
207. Harry
hero
fear
207. Harry's*
cowboy*
mitt
helper*
208. she'll*
209. seem*
210. claws
211. falling*
212. —
213. someone's*
manhole*
214. —
215. —
216. pocketful*
pigs
pig*
oranges*
corn *
217. trade
218. trading*
sold
219. returning
bottles
empty
bottle*
return*
220. shoveling
shoveled*
shovel*
mothers*
few
cents
draw
letters*
able
221. nickel
perhaps
222. piles*
taken*
223. wagon
worker*
224. Benjamin
whenever*
Benjamin's*
225. —
226. west
227. California
Watertown*
228. fiddler
hills*
fiddle*
229. fishing*
supper
traveler
minute
fiddler's*
230. excuse
staying*
fix*
moment
231. spoke
shining
chased*
232. notes*
233. snake
snakes*
leader
234. rocks
YEOW
235. yelled
236. grassy*
leaves
shouts*
237. thirsty
scout

238. Natural
History
scouts*

239. Rachel
runner*
added

240. Mom
captain
boys'*
players*
Rachel's*
girls'*
Charles'*

241. pitcher
pitch*

242. pitched*

243. Mac
lazy
laziest*
opens*

244. wakes*
escape
Mac's*
onto*
fence

245. bangs*
throws*

246. engine
engines*
rush*

247. climbs*

248. wishes*

249. beneath
stony*

250. —

251. Washington, D.C.